Your Pilot's License

YOUR PILOT'S LICENSE

by
CLAY JOHNSON
AND
JOE CHRISTY

CROWN PUBLISHERS, INC.   NEW YORK

ACKNOWLEDGMENT

The authors wish to offer a bouquet of tailwinds to Flight Instructors Arch E. Parks and Clyde W. Fincher, who patiently read this book in preparation and provided many helpful suggestions and criticisms.

Clay Johnson
and
Joe Christy

Contents

I
The Airplane

The Airplane

WHAT HOLDS IT UP?

Wings may be long or short, wide or narrow, but one thing they all have in common is *camber*. This is the term used to describe the curved cross section. Viewed from the side, the lightplane wing is shaped like this:

1. LIGHTPLANE AIRFOIL: The shape produces the lift.

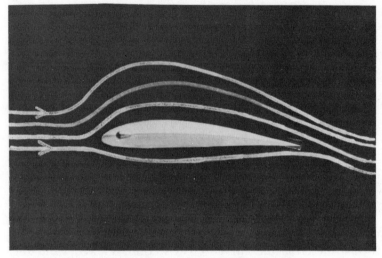

2. NORMAL AIRFLOW PATTERN.

The curved upper surface produces most of the lift. This is because, in flight, air is forced to separate at the leading edge and come together again at the trailing edge. Naturally, the air flowing over the curved top surface has farther to travel in order to meet the air flowing under the bottom of the wing; therefore, this air above has to thin out and speed up. This causes an area of low pressure on top, into which the wing is constantly drawn. Figure 2 shows how this air path would look if air were visible.

Lift is increased by tipping the leading edge upward and adding a deflection force from underneath to the partial vacuum above the wing. However, the extent to which the wing may be tilted upward is limited; for obviously if it is turned at too great an angle to the oncoming air, the flow over the top surface will be interrupted and the low-pressure area will disappear, taking your lift with it. If this happens, the wing is "stalled," and the airflow looks like this:

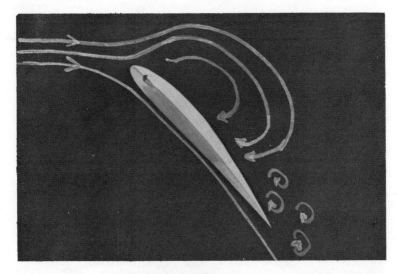

3. STALL: Flow of air over upper surface is interrupted and lifting force disappears.

ANGLE OF ATTACK:

Everything an airplane does in flight depends upon the angle at which the leading edge of the wing strikes the supporting sea of air. This air flowing around the wings is called *relative wind*. Remember this term; it's the whole story of flight. The angle at which the wing strikes the air is your *angle of attack,* and the wind created by your forward movement is *relative wind*.

The popular saying, "He lost flying speed and stalled," is misleading. A plane is easily stalled at its top speed, as any pilot will tell you. Simply increase the *angle of attack* past its critical point, causing the *relative wind* to strike the wing well below the leading edge—then regardless of speed, the air can no longer flow around the lifting surfaces in the smooth pattern necessary to produce lift. This condition can occur in *any* attitude: a turn, climb, dive pullout, etc.

CENTER OF GRAVITY:

An airplane is a balanced machine and rotates three ways about its center of gravity. As shown in figure 4, these axes converge at the center of gravity, which is, in effect, the balance point of the airplane. This is why there are limits, not only as to amount, but also as to placing of loads within the airplane.

The center of lift is in the low-pressure area on top of the wing.

4. AXES: Plane "rolls" about longitudinal axis, "pitches" (nose up or down) about horizontal axis, and "yaws" (nose right or left) about perpendicular axis.

THE FLIGHT CONTROL SYSTEM:

Primary flight controls—wheel and rudder pedals—are connected to the movable surfaces on the wings and tail by steel cable or mechanical linkage. They work the same way on a lightplane as they do on an airliner or a jet.

When the wheel is pushed forward, the elevators are lowered and the nose is pushed away from the pilot; wheel back, the elevators are raised and the nose pulled toward the pilot.

5. FLIGHT CONTROL SURFACES: *A*, ailerons; *S*, horizontal stabilizer; *E*, elevators; *R*, rudder; *V*, vertical stabilizer.

Another way of thinking of it is that forward and backward movement of the wheel controls your *angle of attack:* forward movement *decreases* the angle, and backward pressure *increases* it.

You should think of your *throttle* as the "up and down" control because, although backward movement of the wheel will *point* the nose upward, it is the engine that *takes* you upward.

Turning your wheel to right or left banks the airplane in a corresponding direction. Turn wheel to right, and you raise the aileron on the right wing while simultaneously lowering the aileron on the left wing. The airflow over the wings then forces down the right wing and lifts the left one.

The rudder is not *the* turn control; it is only one of them. Ailerons and rudder *together* produce a balanced turn. If you press your right rudder pedal while holding your wings level, the nose will *point* to the right, but you'll skid straight ahead.

Similarly, if you bank to the right (or left) while holding the nose straight ahead, you will "slip"—tip on one wing and lose altitude—but you won't turn. So, use rudder and wheel *together* to accomplish turns. In other words, turns are made by the interplay of forces resulting from co-ordinated wheel and rudder-pedal pressures.

You will not ride the controls around a turn. After the slight pressures are applied to establish the turn, your controls will be returned to neutral, except for a tiny back-pressure required to compensate for the slight "G"-force caused by your change of direction.

This "G"-force, which pushes you down in the seat during a turn, is in direct proportion to the steepness (quickness) of the turn. In a normal turn of a 30-degree bank or less, it is very slight. In a steeply banked turn it is more pronounced. But this same force is pushing down on your plane, therefore the wings must have proportionately more lift to make up for it. Back pressure on the wheel increases your angle of attack and gives you this extra lift, thus preventing loss of altitude during the turn.

THE THROTTLE:

Your throttle is that big knob at the bottom-center of the instrument panel. Pulled all the way out, it is at idle; pushed all the way in, it is "wide open." The knurled collar on the throttle shaft is a friction-lock which makes it easy to set the "gas" at any desired position. Also on the shaft is a little groove which marks the cruise setting, and this is to make things easier for you too.

PROPELLER TORQUE:

As air is dragged through the turning prop blades, it is given a spiraling motion. This twisting column of air exerts a sidewise pressure on the fuselage and pushes upward against the lower left wing. (This is why the bottom of the left wing gets clobbered with bugs while the bottom of the right wing remains clean.) The prop also exerts a reaction on the engine and its mounting (Newton's Law of Equal and Opposite Force), and these combined forces tend to rotate the plane in an opposite direction. At normal cruise this is seldom noticed because the plane is rigged to compensate for it; but at greater or lower throttle settings a little rudder pressure usually is needed to maintain a straight course.

Wing Flaps:

Wing flaps are hinged to the inboard sides of the wings along the trailing edge. Although some people think of them as "speed reducers," they are, primarily, "lift increasers." This is because they change the *camber* of the wing, increasing its lifting ability, and for this reason their use allows a plane to approach for a landing at a steeper angle. Also, the additional lift makes them valuable for shortening take-off runs out of cramped places.

Stabilizer:

The horizontal stabilizer is the front portion of the horizontal tail surface. (The back parts are the hinged elevators, of course.) By winding the leading edge of the stabilizer up and down—thus changing its angle of attack—the tail can be made to ride high or low. This is useful in trimming the plane to compensate for varying loads. A properly trimmed airplane will fly itself without help from the pilot.

The Engine:

Airplanes have been powered with everything from steam to diesel; but as a civilian pilot, the only power plants you're likely to encounter are the air-cooled, four-cycle, gasoline engines, similar in principle to the one in your car. These

6. FLAPS: Extended flaps increase wings' lifting ability, allowing
slower flight and steeper glide approach.

engines have their cylinders lying aproximately opposite one
another, horizontally, with the crankshaft in the center. For
extra safety and dependability, each cylinder has two spark
plugs; in fact, there are really two separate ignition systems.

Magnetos are used to supply "fire" for the combustion
chambers. (A storage battery is carried too, for the operation
of electrical accessories and for starting the engine.) A magneto is a generator, turned by means of a drive shaft from the
engine, and the faster the engine runs, the hotter the spark
the mag furnishes. Since there are two ignition systems, there
are two magnetos, controlled by the switch in the cockpit.
This switch has four positions: *Off, Left, Right,* and *Both.*
The *Left* and *Right* position of the switch allows us to test
each ignition system separately, although the engine is always
operated on *Both.* This switch is comparable to the ignition
switch in your car and uses a key resembling your car key.

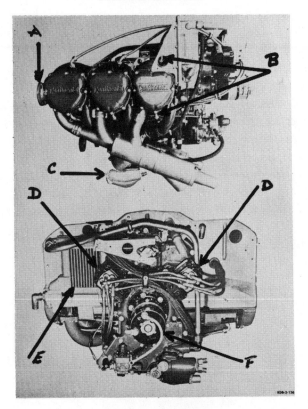

7. LIGHTPLANE ENGINE: *A*, prop hub; *B*, spark plugs; *C*, carburetor intake; *D*, magnetos; *E*, oil cooling radiator; *F*, starter.

PROPELLERS:

In cross section, a propeller is shaped like a wing. It produces "lift" just as the wing does, except in a different direction. And this is why it is desirable to be able to change its pitch in order to gain more, or less, "pull" from it. Changing a prop's pitch actually just changes its angle of attack. Most of the smaller engines swing fixed-pitch props, however, because of the lightplane's limited load-capacity and its narrow speed range. They are made of metal or laminated wood.

The *variable-pitch* prop is one that may be adjusted to two or more angles of attack while the prop is at rest.

The *controllable-pitch* type may be adjusted in flight by means of a control in the cockpit.

The *constant-speed* prop will turn at a constant rpm setting selected by the pilot, and it automatically adjusts its own pitch to compensate for varying load conditions.

While on the ground, a propeller is dangerous. *Never* start your engine without *knowing* that no one is in front of the plane, and always shout, "Clear!" before pressing the starter button. Don't trust a prop at rest, because a "short" in the switch system can easily furnish enough juice to start the engine if the prop is turned by hand.

8(a). CONSTANT-SPEED PROP: Operated hydraulically, this prop maintains constant rpm by automatically adjusting its own pitch to compensate for varying aircraft attitudes.

8(b). FIXED-PITCH PROP: Most lightplanes swing a fixed-pitch prop. This one is metal, attached to a 165 h.p. Franklin engine in the nose of a Stinson Station Wagon. The Stinson is no longer manufactured, but there are a lot of them still flying.

INSTRUMENTS:

Your basic instruments are the *airspeed, altimeter, tachometer,* and the *turn-bank indicator.* We'll talk about these and a couple of engine gauges now, then take up the compass when we go into navigation.

The *oil-pressure gauge* is important in an airplane for the same reason it is in any other machine dependent upon pressure lubrication. Upon starting your engine, this is the gauge you'll watch. It should move up into the safe operating range within the first half-minute of engine operation.

The *oil-temperature gauge* serves your plane as the water temperature gauge does your car, but you should pay more attention to it than you do its automobile counterpart. For example, a cold engine will not deliver full power, and with the throttle wide open, as on take-off, it can cut out altogether. This can be mighty inconvenient.

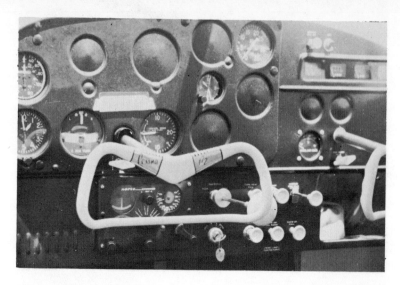

9(a). (*above*) FLIGHT INSTRUMENTS: This is the panel of the popular Cessna 172. Top left is airspeed. Bottom, left to right: altimeter, turn-bank indicator, rate-of-climb. Right center, clock. Upper right, tachometer. Engine gauges are on right panel. 9(b). (*below*) FLIGHT INSTRUMENTS: This is a "full panel"—everything needed for instrument flight—installed in a Piper Caribbean. Above the cowl is the magnetic compass with its deviation card. Flight instruments are on left panel. Left to right, top row: airspeed, gyrocompass, artificial horizon. Bottom row of left panel: clock, altimeter, turn-bank, and rate-of-climb. Take-off check list is printed in center of left panel. Center panel contains VHF radio above, Low Frequency radio below. Right panel holds engine gauges. They are, top row, left to right: tachometer, manifold pressure, ammeter. Bottom right panel: oil pressure and temperature, plus a fuel gauge for each wing tank.

9(c). (*above*) SUPER CUB COCKPIT: A glance at the "front office" of the ubiquitous Cub reveals its functional simplicity. The throttle knob is just below the window on the left side. Instruments are, left to right: tachometer, airspeed, compass, altimeter, oil pressure and oil temperature. Panel-knob on left side is mixture control, panel-knob on right, engine primer. Rear seat has duplicate stick, throttle, and rudder pedals. 10. (*below*) PITOT TUBE: Some are heated to prevent blockage by ice in flight. *Not* designed for use as coat rack.

The *tachometer* shows the revolutions per minute (rpm) that the engine turns. On lightplanes, tachs are mechanically driven by means of a flexible shaft similar to an automobile speedometer cable.

The *airspeed* is a pressure instrument which measures the velocity of the air past the plane. It is actually a barometer, with its dial registering the difference between motionless air and the pressure resulting from the impact of air at the opening of a small tube. This tube is placed outside of the prop blast—usually in the left wing—and is called the *Pitot tube*.

You should understand that this instrument is not a speed-ometer. It merely shows the velocity of air over the wings—the speed at which you are moving through the air—and does not take into account winds that can make your speed over the ground a very different thing. Also, it doesn't even tell the truth about airspeed. Since it is a pressure instrument, varying air densities will cause it to indicate falsely. Air density lessens with altitude, therefore add two per cent per thousand feet to correct for this. And since heated air is less dense, a correction must be made for temperature.

The *altimeter* is another barometer, with its dial calibrated in feet. It works on the principle that air pressure decreases steadily with altitude. However, since heated air is thinner than cold air, a correction must be made for temperature in order to obtain an accurate reading. This correction—like the temperature correction required for airspeed readings—is obtained from a simple, circular slide-rule called a *computer* (and which pilots, naturally, call a "confuser").

Since natural barometric pressure changes often, the altimeter must be set to compensate for local conditions. This is done by means of a knob beneath the instrument which rotates a small dial set in the face. The altimeter settings given from the tower or the weather office are the barometric pressures corrected to sea level. Therefore, when you adjust your altimeter to that reading, it will correspond to the altitude of that particular airport. In other words, it measures your height above sea level, not above the ground. Always set your altimeter before each flight.

In practice, set your altimeter to correspond with the elevation of the field from which you are taking off. In doing this, the little window in its face will then show the corrected sea-level pressure. If this reading does not agree with the barometric pressure given from the tower, then you know there is an error in your instrument.

The *turn-bank indicator* is really two instruments in one. The ball-bank looks and works like a carpenter's level. It is your slip and skid indicator. As long as the ball remains centered, your maneuvers are well co-ordinated. The turn-needle is controlled by a gyro, and it shows your rate of turn.

Pictured below is the panel of a modern lightplane. You will note that the flight instruments are grouped together in front of the pilot. Engine gauges are on the right.

11. PRIMARY PANEL: Compass and compass deviation card above cowl. Top row, left to right: airspeed, turn-bank, space for gyro-compass, radio. Bottom row, left to right, space for clock, altimeter (note altimeter-set knob), tachometer, oil pressure and oil temperature. Ignition switch, throttle, and mixture control are below in center, between the dual control wheels.

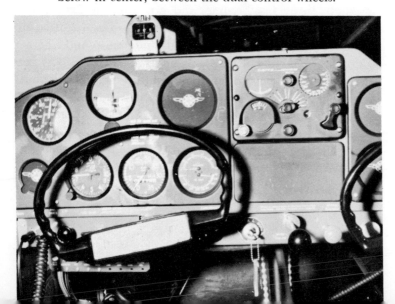

12. PIPER CARIBBEAN: Three Nine Delta, the plane we'll fly in this book.

She's beautiful, isn't she? No other machine stands so confidently poised, or possesses such sleekness of line. And properly handled she's as graceful in flight as she looks.

A lot ot "prop-wash" has been written about how simple—or tough—flying has become, and how safe—or dangerous—airplanes are to fly. It doesn't mean much. The truth is, airplanes are neither safe nor dangerous—*pilots* are. And whether or not flying is difficult depends upon perspective. *Any* reasonably normal person can learn to fly with eight or ten hours of competent, dual instruction. This will not make you a professional pilot, but you'll be able to take off, fly, and land safely. From that point, everything depends upon the standards you adopt, for, as in all areas of human accomplishment, the rewards are in proportion to the effort invested and the goal established.

If you are a perfectionist, you will constantly do two things in an airplane which most of us find difficult. First, you'll learn to *relax*. Second, *think!*

An airplane is an extremely forgiving machine. She *wants* to fly and, properly trimmed, will do so without help. She will do "what comes naturally" (true to her gender, however, she will not be concerned with where she is going or how her fuel supply is planned), but due to the lightplane's inherently stable characteristics pilots too lazy to think fall into sloppy flying habits. They dope off and, sitting up there "fat, dumb, and happy," manage to get themselves into various kinds of trouble.

Getting back to this relaxing business and why your flight instructor will mention it so often: The physical sensations of flight are centered in your stomach muscles. During any change of direction the forces acting upon the plane, and you, will be most noticeable in the solar plexus region. If these muscles are tense, their very valuable assistance in helping you to co-ordinate the controls smoothly will be lost. When you take over the controls for the first time, grip the wheel lightly; rest your feet lightly on the rudder pedals. Compared to the force required to turn your car, almost none is needed to turn your plane. She's sensitive, so remember: Be always alert, but not tense.

THE PREFLIGHT CHECK:

If you have spent any time around an airport, watching different pilots wheel out their planes and take off, you may have observed that some carefully and suspiciously inspect their craft before getting in to start the engine. Others do not. Well, this is the easiest way in the world to tell the Old Pilots from the Bold Pilots—there are no Old Bold Pilots. There is no more important "maneuver" in flying than the preflight check, nor is any taught for a better reason.

Come along now for your first lesson. We'll take this

saucy four-place job with the tricycle landing gear, and we'll begin with the preflight check:

13(a). PREFLIGHT CHECK: This maneuver separates the Old Pilots from the Bold Pilots.

Let's start here at the left (port) wingtip. Look for tip damage. Continuing along the trailing edge, inspect the aileron for freedom of movement. Check each hinge, nut, and safety key. Check the control cable leading from the aileron, and look over the top of the wing for any sign of damage there. We'll give the wingflap a similar check, glance at the wing-fillet for loose screws, then go to the tail for hinge inspection. Walking on around the plane counterclockwise, we'll perform a similar ritual along the trailing edge of the right (starboard) wing. Check the leading edge and the tire on this side. We'll *visually* check the amount of gas in each wing tank and be sure the cap is secured on each. Inspect the prop spinner, and look over the prop blades for nicks and

13(b). PREFLIGHT CHECK: Check the oil dipstick.

dents. Reaching beneath the nose—at the rear of the engine—turn the little petcock which drains the fuel-sediment bowl. Then just inboard of the right landing-gear strut on the plane's belly there's a small opening with another petcock. This drains the gas line at its lowest point, so empty that ounce or so of fuel onto the ground also. Next, raise the cowl on the right side and check the oil dipstick. Be sure to replace it. Check the ignition harness, and look for cracks in the exhaust manifold. Repeat this procedure on the other side and, after making sure that the cowl snaps are locked, wind up your preflight check at your starting point at the left wingtip.

Now, let's get into the airplane. You'll sit in the pilot's seat on the left. Put your foot on the step and, with your right hand, take hold of the brace behind the windshield and swing into the seat. *Don't* pull yourself in by the control wheel. And right now—before you do another thing—is the time to fasten your seat belt. Comfortable? O.K. Here are the things we'll do before we start the engine:

Be sure the parking brake is set. The brake lever is below the dash, just under the throttle. To set the brakes, pull the lever back and pull out the *brake set* knob on the panel just to the left of the control wheel.

The *master switch* is a toggle-type and is below your left leg on the front of the seat. Snap it up to turn it on. This will cause your fuel gauges to register.

The fuel tank *selector switch* is on the left wall below the dash. Its positions are *Left, Right,* and *Off.* Turn it to the tank which you are to use—the fullest one.

Push the *fuel mixture* knob completely in. This gives you a rich mixture, which you always want for landing and take-off. This knob is at the bottom of the dash on your right.

Set the dashboard clock.

Set your altimeter.

Above your head is a crank with an indicator saying, *"Nose: Up—Down."* This is the stabilizer control. Set it in neutral.

The *carburetor heat* knob is directly in front of you on the dashboard. Set it at *Cold.*

About that carburetor heat control: The throat of your carburetor is venturi-shaped. The fuel-air mixture entering the carb throat is first compressed, then it expands rapidly while headed for the intake manifold. Any gas—including plain air—gets very cold when rapidly expanded. The suction through your carb can drop the air temperature as much as forty degrees; therefore, ice can form in the carb throat when the outside air temperature is anywhere between 25° and 70° F. It shouldn't cause you any trouble, because the signs of carb ice are easy to recognize: rpm's will begin to drop; the engine will run rough and choke down. The carbu-

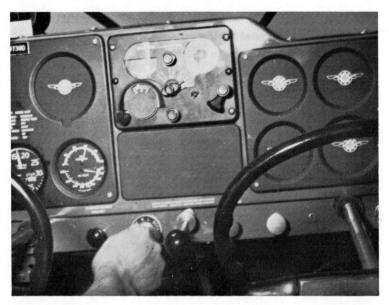

14. PRE-TAKE-OFF MAGNETO CHECK: Open throttle to 1,700 rpm (note tachometer), and flip ignition switch to "L," then "R." Watch tach for rpm drop.

retor heat knob is so handy that this condition need never become very far advanced.

We don't like to use carb heat for landing and take-off because it decreases the volume of fuel mixture through the intake and robs us of power. You will understand of course that regardless of air temperature, the relative humidity must be fairly high before carb icing is probable.

IN THE AIR:

Well, your *master switch* still on? O.K., just beneath it is the *starter* button.

Open your window and call, "Clear!"

With the throttle knob in the palm of your hand, lay your right forefinger along the shaft with your nail about an eighth of an inch from the stop. Now, push in the throttle just that much. Almost no throttle is needed to start the engine. Press the starter button and reach to the dash, turning the magneto switch to *Both*.

She starts at once, but you'll notice that she's idling pretty fast, so inch the throttle back toward you and slow her down to a respectable idle.

Watch the oil-pressure gauge, and as it comes up out of the red zone, you're ready to taxi. Release the parking brake.

Applying a little power, start the plane rolling straight ahead and turn while the plane is in motion (turning from a standstill is hard on tires). Keep your right hand on the throttle and your left one in your lap; otherwise, you'll have a tendency to try to steer with the wheel, and the wheel won't turn you on the ground. Your nose wheel is linked with the rudder pedals, and therefore ground steering is done with the feet.

Before rolling onto the runway, turn as near into the wind as practicable. Set the parking brake and perform the following pre-take-off check:

a) Verify oil temperature and oil pressure.

b) Open throttle to 1700 rpm tach reading, and turning the magneto switch to "L," watch the tach for loss of rpm's. It will drop some, but the drop should not exceed 100 rpm's. Switch back to "Both," to allow the rpm's to build up again, then switch to "R" and check that system.

c) *Carefully* check for incoming planes. A good trick is to swing the plane in a complete circle so that you can get an unobstructed view of the entire pattern. No traffic? Fine. Reach above your head there and wind the stabilizer several turns toward the *Nose Up* position. She'll climb at her normal rate without your having to hold back on the wheel. We're ready to aviate.

Roll into take-off position and line up with the runway. Smoothly push the throttle forward to Full Open. Maintain a straight course with the rudder pedals. She picks up speed rapidly; so as soon as you have good response to the elevators, ease back on the wheel and lift the nose wheel off. Now gradually increase back-pressure. There, you're airborne.

The nose is swinging a little to one side because you're not correcting for torque. Give her a little rudder.

15. (*above*) FUEL TANK SELECTOR: On left wall, below dash, the selector switch determines from which of the two wing tanks fuel is to be used. 16. (*below*) TAKE OFF: Throttle is wide open. Maintain straight course with rudder pedals. Gently ease back control wheel.

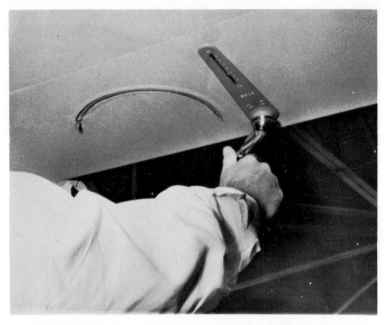

17. Trim: Wind stabilizer four or five turns toward "nose up" position and she'll climb without help.

Her best climbing speed is around 90 mph.

You'll quickly become accustomed to the effects of each control, and it is best for you to put them out of your mind as you do. In other words, fly the plane instead of the controls. Put a wing down, push the nose away, etc., rather than think of maneuvers in terms of control movements.

You'll have a tendency at first to overcontrol; but don't worry about this, because you are probably used to driving a car, where a lot of "control movement" is needed. You'll soon get used to the light, small pressures required for controlling your plane. Just remember, she's a sensitive and high-spirited critter.

As you enter a turn, rudder and aileron pressures are ap-

18. (*above*) RIGHT TURN: Note that aileron is back to neutral after turn is established. 19. (*below*) LEFT TURN: Looking forward over the nose.

20. LEFT GLIDING TURN: Looking forward through the prop from 4,500 feet.

plied simultaneously—co-ordinated—then, as the bank and rate-of-turn become established, the aileron and rudder are returned to neutral (because if you continue to put pressure on the wheel and rudder pedal, the turn will continue to steepen). In steep turns, a good deal of back-pressure on the wheel may be required all the way around the turn, but don't forget that back-pressure on the wheel always increases your angle of attack, and no matter how much speed you've got, you can pull the wing into an unflyable angle if you get the wheel back too far.

Another thing about steep turns: As you tip your wing sharply down on one end, its lift is no longer opposite the pull of gravity. The lift is still there, but it is at an angle to the force of gravity. In a 90° bank, you paste yourself against the sky with your wings pulling inward toward the center of the circle you are making. You are at an extremely high angle of attack, and it requires an awful lot of speed to execute such a turn—assuming that your plane is stressed for such stuff, and the wings don't come unstuck! In this attitude, your plane and you weigh over *six* times as much as in level flight! Therefore, we offer this advice: Keep the load off yourself, and you won't overload the airplane.

21. (*above*) WING LOAD: The load on the wings increases as the angle of bank increases. In a 20° bank, you and your plane weigh 1.06 normal. 22. (*below*) FORTY-DEGREE BANK: You and your craft weigh nearly one-third more than normal in this attitude.

23. EIGHTY-DEGREE BANK: In this kind of turn you are pulling almost 6 "G's"—wings must support 5.76 normal weight.

STALL RECOVERY:

How do you know when you are about to stall? Well, sound is a good indication. The sound of the air past the plane will lower in pitch. Controls loosen up, and there is a lag in control response. Loss of aileron control usually comes first, because ailerons are outside the prop wash. In some planes there is a noticeable tail-buffeting. And of course there is the airspeed indicator staring at you. The modern lightplane, however, is so honest that her stall habits are gentle and next to foolproof. Let's do a stall and see. With the throttle cut back to idle, bring the wheel all the way back, clear to the stops. She'll slow up rapidly, and a glance at the airspeed will probably startle you. It's bumping nervously at 40 mph! You'll feel just the slightest tremble in the wheel as she reaches full stall (that's the airflow burbling over the top of the wing), but she'll merely tuck her nose down a little, sink a few feet, recover for just a second or two, and then, if you've still "got 'er by the throat," will repeat this until you let go of the wheel and allow her to seek a flyable angle of attack. We did this in order to show you that today's lightplane is a lady under the worst conditions—there was even good aileron response during the stall and no tendency to spin. Because of the modern lightplane's good behavior, spins are no longer a part of the license examination.

Except for practice, there is no reason why you should deliberately stall your plane in flight, but you'll receive ample instruction in stall recovery as a safety measure. The best procedure in case you inadvertently stall is to release back-pressure on the wheel and apply power.

LANDING:

You've accumulated appreciable altitude, so we'll have a long letdown. Cut back the throttle to idle, a fast idle, and adjust your glide with the wheel at about 80 mph. If you'll give the stabilizer crank about 5 turns toward the *Nose Up* arrow, she'll glide hands-off. In cool weather a long glide may cause the engine to overcool, so watch the oil-temperature gauge. Also, "clear" the engine with the throttle occasionally to prevent the cylinders from loading up with fuel.

Plan your approach so that you will enter the traffic pattern at an altitude of 800 feet above the surface. Your normal glide will then dissipate your remaining altitude during the completion of the pattern. "Play" your turn onto the base leg to compensate for weak or strong wind, and the length of your final approach will also be determined by wind velocity. In other words, landing into a relatively strong wind, your pattern will be "tighter." If the wind is light or calm, you will fly a longer downwind leg; your base leg will be farther from the strip, and your final approach longer.

Coming in over the end of the runway, break your glide with back-pressure on the wheel (this is called the flare-out), at about 10 or 12 feet above the surface. Hold the nose high after your flare-out, and touch down on the two main wheels. Steer with the rudder, holding the wheel well back, and as she loses speed, the nose wheel will ease down. Let the speed drop as much as practicable before applying the brakes. Don't ride the brakes, and never use them before the nose wheel is down.

Once you have throttled back and established a glide for your landing approach, you have also established the maximum distance you can cover before touching the ground. In other words, nothing you can do with the wheel and rudder pedals will add one inch to that distance. If you notice on your final that you're about to undershoot a few feet, then *open the throttle* to get the few feet. That natural tendency to pull back on the wheel will get your nose up all right, but without power it will merely slow you down and cause you to sink faster.

Pictured below is a typical landing pattern. Always enter and leave the pattern at a 45° angle so that you can be sure that you're not crowding someone. Also, enter the downwind leg at least halfway down the field so you won't be congesting traffic by meeting planes which have just taken-off.

24. ENTERING LANDING PATTERN: Enter pattern at 45° angle so that you may best observe other traffic. Strip is visible just above cowl. We'll land right to left.

25. (*above*) DOWNWIND LEG: We are paralleling the strip, flying in the opposite direction from that in which we'll land. We are about 800 feet above the surface. Our altimeter, which registers sea level altitude, indicates slightly over 1,900 feet. 26. (*below*) BASE LEG: We are gliding at about 90 mph indicated airspeed. A left turn from the downwind leg has put us at a right angle to the runway and far enough away to make our final approach at least 1,000 feet long.

27. FINAL APPROACH: Another left turn lines us up with the runway for our final approach. The DC-3 waiting on the taxi strip will not take off until we are down. Landing aircraft always have right of way.

If a landing approach goes sour for any reason, don't hesitate to open your throttle and go around again. Early recognition of the need to go around is important to insure a safe margin of altitude and speed. The airport gang will have a lot more respect for your good judgment in playing it safe than they have for the vanity which prompts a few pilots to attempt salvage of a bad approach.

After landing, clear the runway immediately.

CIVIL AIR REGULATIONS:

Before you are allowed to solo—which will come usually after about 8 or 10 hours of instruction at a cost of about $15 an hour—you will have to get a medical certificate from a local doctor designated by the Federal Aviation Agency (FAA). The physical this doctor will give you is not a tough one, though if you wear glasses you will be required to keep

them on at all times when flying. Special disability waivers
are often allowed for people without an arm or leg; and we
know at least one fellow who, unable to use either leg, has
rigged an electric winch to lift him into the cockpit of his
Fornaire. (The Fornaire has a unique control system: Rudder
and ailerons are interconnected, and there are no rudder
pedals.) Besides the physical, you will also have to pass a
written exam on air traffic rules—about like the one you take
for an automobile driver's test.

Completion of these two things will get you your *Student's
Permit*. After solo, you may not carry passengers on your
Student's Permit. The sole purpose of this permit is to allow
you to fly alone while building up the minimum air time to
qualify you for your Pilot's License Examination.

Technically, you are eligible for your Private Ticket with
a minimum of 35 hours, but you'll probably have 40 hours
before asking the FAA safety agent to give you your test.

After your license has been issued, you are required to
renew your medical certificate every 24 months.

You are eligible for a Commercial Pilot's License (which
will allow you to fly for pay) when you have a minimum of
200 logged hours. This physical is a little tougher and is
required every 12 months. Also, the safety agent will be more
exacting in his check-ride with you. The written part of this
exam is chiefly concerned with navigation and weather recognition.

The Airline Transport License puts you in the top pro
class. Frankly, it's pretty difficult to obtain, and the physical
is repeated every 6 months.

Ratings, which are special qualifications added to your
license, include Instrument Rating, Multi-engine, Seaplane,
Flight Instructor, and Ground Instructor. A separate test
must be passed for each.

Log Book:

You are required to maintain a Pilot's Log, and although all flight time need not be entered, such time as needed toward license and ratings must be listed.

Right-of-Way:

When two aircraft are on converging courses at nearly the same altitude, the plane on the right has the right-of-way. When two airplanes are approaching head-on, each must give way to the right, and they shall not pass closer than 500 feet. In landing approaches, the lowest plane has the right-of-way unless another is making an emergency landing. Landing aircraft always have the right-of-way over those about to take-off. This is all just common sense, isn't it? Courtesy in the air is just as rewarding safety-wise as it is on the ground.

Legal altitudes for cross-country flying are listed on the reverse sides of all air charts. We'll give them in the section on Navigation a little later.

Most airports have a lefthand (counterclockwise) traffic pattern; but there are a few—due to tall buildings or other obstructions—which have a righthand pattern (clockwise). Where this latter situation exists, there will be a flashing amber light on the control tower and/or a large right-angled marker near the wind indicator on the field.

Legal Papers:

Your airplane's registration and its certificate of airworthiness must be kept in the plane at all times. This airworthiness ticket must be renewed yearly with the FAA agent's inspection of your plane.

You are required to show your pilot's license and your medical certificate to any FAA safety agent or to any law enforcement officer upon demand.

VFR AND IFR:

All flying is either *Visual Flight Rules* or *Instrument Flight Rules*. When flying on the gauges, a *flight plan* is mandatory. This is a form you'll fill out before take-off, listing your destination, possible alternate, and other pertinent data about your trip. In a pinch, flight plans may be radioed to the FAA Airway Communication Station nearest you.

Flying VFR you are pretty much on your own. Minimum visibility for VFR flights is one mile.

Visibility is defined as the average horizontal distance that prominent objects may be seen from the cockpit.

Ceiling is defined as the distance from the surface to the lowest cloud layer or broken overcast.

A flight plan is not required for VFR flights, but extended trips, especially over rough or sparsely populated terrain, should be made with a flight plan. Then if you are ever forced down, the Air Search and Rescue people will turn things upside down to find you. A word of caution: Be sure that you close your flight plan upon reaching your destination. Otherwise, search begins automatically!

CONTROL AREAS AND ZONES:

The airspace above 700 feet lying within a civil airway is called a *control area*.

The airspace in the vicinity of an airport and the airport ground boundary itself are controlled by the airport control tower and are called *control zones*.

Both are clearly marked on all air charts.

II
Weather

Weather

Weather information is free to all pilots at any U.S. Weather Office and, in addition, is broadcast at 15 minutes after the hour and 15 minutes before the hour on the Airway Communications radios. This information is revised and brought up to date every hour—oftener when special conditions exist.

Air Pressure:

Air is densest at sea level. There, it weighs about $1\frac{1}{4}$ ounces per cubic foot and presses down with a pressure of about 14.7 pounds per square inch. This will cause mercury in a vacuum tube to rise 29.92 inches under normal conditions, and so we consider a barometric reading of 29.92 as the reference point or starting point for any fluctuation in pressure.

You are concerned with all this because several of your most important flight instruments are pressure gauges, because air is the medium in which a flyer operates, and because variations in pressure are linked with variations in weather.

Now if temperatures remained constant, there wouldn't be much to this pressure business, but of course they don't. The sun heats the earth's surface unequally. Different kinds of terrain absorb or reflect heat rays differently.

Here's what happens. The air next to the ground becomes heated by contact with the warm earth and the reflected rays of the sun. This air expands and becomes lighter, causing it to rise. (These rising columns of air are called thermal or convection currents.) Naturally, if a parcel of air expands and rises over a given place, the pressure there is going to decrease. Therefore we say that a *low-pressure area* exists. And the higher-pressure air surrounding this Low wants to rush in and equalize things. Thus, a wind is born.

High-pressure areas owe their existence to just the opposite causes. Air gets denser and heavier when it is cooled. Cool air is stable * and clear. This is why, as a flyer, you will always associate Highs with good flying conditions and always suspect Lows of harboring bad weather.

It should be noted that when we speak of "warm" and "cool" air, the meaning of the adjectives is relative. If temperature at a given place is 90° and the place is surrounded with air of 85°, then this 85° is "cool."

The winds around a Low are counterclockwise; around a High, they rotate clockwise. This is because the higher pressure air surrounding a Low, flowing inward to equalize pressure, is deflected to one side by the earth's rotation from west to east. The air moving outward from a High is also given a twist by the earth's spin, which causes these winds to blow just opposite to those around a Low. These processes are reversed south of the Equator.

FRONTS AND AIR MASSES:

There are really only two basic kinds of air masses: *tropical* and *polar.* In order to know what to expect when one starts moving, however, the weather people further classify them according to the route they travel and their relative temper-

---

* Stable air, to the weatherman, is air in which cumulus will not build up into thunderheads. Many pilots call bumpy air "unstable," although from the meteorologist's point of view just the opposite may be the case. For example, the cool air behind a cold front may be bumpy—it usually is—but nevertheless it is stable.

atures. Their route is significant because air flowing over continents will not pick up moisture as will air traveling over oceans. Therefore when an air mass begins to move, the weatherman tags it first according to its origin and second according to its route. Third, he labels it "warm" or "cold," and this is determined solely by comparing its temperature with the air it is moving in on.

We can have, for example, Polar Masses which are sub-labeled Continental or Maritime, and these may be warm or cold. Similarly, we may have Tropical Maritime or Tropical Continental, and either may be warm or cold.

In other words, air masses are named for their origin, route of travel, and their comparative temperature. From these characteristics their behavior may be forecast.

When an air mass starts moving it often produces a *front;* that is, there will be an almost definite line along its foremost part which separates it from the air of different temperature that it is overtaking. (There is surprisingly little mixing together of the air of two different temperatures when they come together.)

A *cold front* then is the boundary line at the surface of the earth which divides a mass of cooler air from the warmer air in its path.

A *warm front* is the dividing line, on the surface, between an advancing mass of warm air and a retreating mass of cooler air.

A cold front presents a wedge-shaped forepart because, being relatively heavy, it pushes under the warmer air in its path. Along this wedge-shaped leading edge the displaced warmer air, being pushed upward, tends to condense and form clouds—high cumulus and thunderheads—and rain or snow may be expected. The cold front has a silver lining though, because the cool air behind it means smooth, stable, and heavy air, with good visibility.

Warm fronts, too, bring a change in weather: usually

precipitation in some form, changing winds, but unlike cold fronts, overcast skies and unstable air. The leading edge of a warm front rides up over the cooler air in its path, forming in reverse the same kind of wedge that occurs at the leading edge of the cold front.

You'll notice that the leading edge of a front is shown on weather maps in respect to its location on the ground. Therefore, while the leading edge of a cold front will be farthest advanced next to the ground, the front edge of a warm front at a height of several thousand feet will be far ahead of the ground line.

HUMIDITY AND DEW POINT:

Dew point is the temperature at which the moisture in the air condenses.

Relative humidity is the ratio of moisture the air contains to the amount of moisture it could contain if saturated at the same temperature. That about as clear as the Mississippi? Well, let's say it this way: For any given amount of moisture in the air, there is a temperature at which it will condense. That temperature is the dew point. Divide dew point by actual temperature to obtain relative humidity. For example, if the temperature is 50 and the dew point 40, then relative humidity would be 80 per cent.

Any time temperature and dew point approach within a degree or so of one another, fog or some other form of precipitation is likely.

LAPSE RATES:

Under normal conditions the temperature of the atmos-

28. (page 53, above) COLD FRONT: These weather systems travel about 300 to 400 miles per day in summer, about 500 miles per 24 hours in winter. 29. (below) WARM FRONT: These systems are usually less violent than cold fronts, although the sky generally remains murky after their passage.

Anatomy of a fast
Cold Front storm

Thunderhead

Scud (cloud fragments

downdrafts

DIRECTION OF STORM

PURGE OF COOL AIR

WARM AIR

Weather map symbol
for Cold Front line

Cross section through a
Warm front Thunderstorm

Warm air climbing frontal slope

Cool air

Warm air mass

rainfall

Weather map symbol
for Warm front

air in wake of storm is hazy, dull

phere decreases three and one-half degrees per thousand feet of altitude. This is known as the normal lapse rate.

When the sun's heat sets up thermal currents, the air within these ascending columns will cool at the rate of five and one-half degrees per thousand feet until it reaches its dew point temperature. (This is known technically as the dry adiabatic lapse rate.)

While the thermal current was rising—cooling at the rate of five and one-half degrees per thousand feet—and before it reached its dew point and formed a cloud, the dew point was decreasing one degree per thousand feet due to expansion of the air. In order to estimate the altitude at which the clouds are forming, we'll subtract that one degree from the five and one-half, leaving us with a net of four and one-half degrees per thousand feet. And here's why this information is useful. We know the ground temperature and the dew point. Say, for example, it's 87° F., and the dew point is given as 68°. This is a difference of nineteen degrees. Dividing 19 by 4½ we get 4.2. The cloud base is 4,200 feet high.

This method of determining cloud-base altitude is valid *only* for cumulus-type clouds; but since *thunderheads* grow from cumulus, and since cumulus pile up ahead of cold fronts, they're often in the weather picture.

CLOUDS:

Basically, there are only three distinct types of clouds: *cirrus, stratus,* and *cumulus.* However, they often combine to form a number of subspecies. We'll break them down this way and follow with a description of each:

Cirrus	(Ci)	
Cirro-stratus	(Cs)	*High Clouds*
Cirro-cumulus	(Cc)	
Alto-stratus	(As)	*Medium Clouds*
Alto-cumulus	(Ac)	

Strato-cumulus   (Sc)
Nimbo-stratus   (Ns)
Cumulus   (Cu)   *Low Clouds*
Cumulo-nimbus (Cb)
Stratus   (St)

Cirrus clouds are the highest of all. They are made up of ice crystals and are commonly called "mare's tails," or "feathers."

Cirro-stratus give the sky a milky look. They are a thin, high haze made up of ice crystals, which often cause a ring of light to appear around the sun or moon. They usually mean that bad weather is on the way.

Cirro-cumulus clouds are formed from cirrus. They are often referred to as "mackerel sky," and following the appearance of cirrus, then cirro-stratus, indicate brewing storm conditions.

Alto-stratus is a dense, grayish sheet, similar to cirro-stratus, but heavier and lower. It is ordinarily followed by rain or snow.

Alto-cumulus is somewhat like cirro-cumulus in appearance, but the globules are bigger and more pronounced. It is often called "buttermilk sky."

Strato-cumulus clouds form in rolls and waves. They are low and dangerous for the flyer because they present icing hazards if the temperature is near freezing. Usually, they are not associated with rain, though mist or drizzle is possible.

Nimbo-stratus is a low, dense, and dark cloud-layer from which steady rain or snow usually falls. It is shapeless and ragged, and in most cases alto-stratus, from which it has formed, lies above.

Cumulus clouds are especially indicative of weather trends. "Cumulus" means "heap," and is a good descriptive term for the fair-weather type which is white and fluffy and forms at the top of a thermal current. However, if the air is un-

30. (*above*) ALTO-CUMULUS: Range between 8,000 and 20,000 feet. Sometimes called "buttermilk sky." 31(a). (*below*) CUMULUS: Here the air is unstable and the cumulus has begun to take on vertical development. Within an hour or so, it will grow into a thunderhead.

31(b). (*above*) Cumulo-nimbus: Thunderheads building up in the distance; beautiful, but extremely dangerous to airplanes. These are young ones, perhaps an hour from maturity, but even at this stage they are full of turbulence and violent vertical winds. Alto-cumulus lie above. 32. (*below*) Cirro-cumulus and cirro-stratus: These are high clouds, made of ice crystals. They are usually above 20,000 feet and often indicate brewing storm conditions.

stable they begin to take on vertical development and build up to great heights—often above 30,000 feet—from their low bases. Then they are called thunderheads (cumulonimbus), and these towering, castle-like beauties are full of turbulence, violent vertical winds, lightning, and hail, and are extremely dangerous to aircraft.

Stratus is an even or uniform layer of low fog or haze not touching the ground.

High clouds are usually above 20,000 feet.

Medium clouds range from 8,000 to 20,000 feet altitude.

Low clouds are below 8,000 feet.

ICING IN FLIGHT:

First, let's say this: Lightplane pilots should stay away from potential icing conditions.

Ice may form on struts, tail, the leading edges of the wings, and on the propeller. It can be one of two kinds: rime ice, which resembles the stuff that gathers around the freezing unit of your refrigerator and flakes off easily, or the hard, clear stuff called glaze ice. Glaze ice can easily unbalance the prop and cause severe engine damage. Either kind may form on the wings, changing their camber and destroying lift.

Icing conditions are likely to be encountered while flying through wet snow, or rain when the temperature is near freezing or slightly above. It can also form as a result of flying through a cloud layer at near-freezing temperature.

If you should find yourself in a level of dangerous, icing conditions, either climb to colder air where the moisture is already frozen, or descend to warmer air. But since this advice is not always easy to follow in a lightplane, the safest bet is to stay clear of probable icing conditions.

THE WEATHER MAP:

All those black, curvy lines on the weather map are lines of equal pressure. They are called *isobars*. Usually, they are

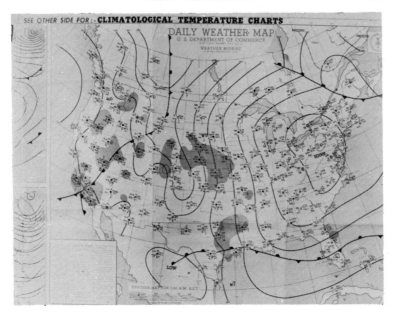

SEE OTHER SIDE FOR:- CLIMATOLOGICAL TEMPERATURE CHARTS
DAILY WEATHER MAP
U S DEPARTMENT OF COMMERCE
WEATHER BUREAU

33. WEATHER MAP: Reporting stations are shown, plus (on this particular day) three different frontal systems. Note that the westernmost front is Maritime Polar in origin, the one in the south, Maritime Tropical.

drawn 3 *millibars* apart. (A millibar is the unit of pressure that meteorologists use instead of inches of mercury, 3 millibars being equal to 1/10th of an inch of mercury.) Since differences in air pressure cause winds, it follows that the closer together the isobars are drawn, the stronger the winds.

Around Lows, the wind direction will be counterclockwise and inward across the isobars at about a 30° angle up to 2,000 feet above the surface. Above this, the winds will parallel the isobars. Around Highs, the wind will be blowing clockwise and outward at about the same angle.

The normal sea-level air-pressure of 29.92 inches of mercury is equal to 1013.2 millibars.

Cold fronts are shown by means of a heavy line with a

saw-toothed edge indicating direction of movement. They travel about 300 to 400 miles per day in summer, about 500 miles per day in winter.

Warm fronts are drawn with little half-moons along the side of the line showing their direction of movement.

Due to the general wind circulation about the world, in the United States we have prevailing westerly winds, and more often than not you can predict tomorrow's weather by noting the weather 400 miles west of you today.

There are several hundred U.S. Weather Reporting Stations which transmit local conditions to the main station in Washington every few hours. This information is correlated and sent back, almost at once. The best weather scientists in the world are working for you. We have yet to meet one who wouldn't bend over backward to assist us in a planned flight.

Each weather office is shown on the map by means of a coded "station model." Pictured below is a typical station

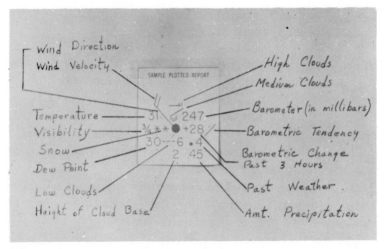

34. WEATHER REPORTING STATION: Most reporting stations seldom include this much information.

model as it would appear on the weather map, along with an explanation of the information it offers.

A *squall line* often precedes a cold front. It is a line of heavy thunderstorms and is indicated on the weather map by a broken line.

The solid gray areas are areas of precipitation.

WINDWARD AND LEEWARD EFFECTS:

On the windward side of a mountain, rapidly moving air will dam up because of the obstruction. This causes an increase in pressure on the windward side, and your altimeter will record a lower altitude than is correct. On the leeward side, the air spills over and washes down, creating a decrease in pressure, and your altimeter will show a greatly higher altitude than you actually have. The danger here is apparent, especially if you're flying above the cloud deck. Also, the downdrafts created on the leeward side add to the danger. A good rule is always to fly at least 2,000 feet higher than the highest peak near your flight path, especially during marginal weather.

III
Air Navigation

Air Navigation

If your airplane is to be a utility machine, you must be able to get into it and go *wherever* you want, *whenever* you want, relying upon your own ability to plot a course and follow it.

35. CROSS-COUNTRY: Point your nose in any direction—the decisions are all yours.

We never heard of anyone who voluntarily quit flying after making a few cross-country flights alone. No other experience matches the freedom of flight; you can point your nose in any direction, and the decisions are all yours! It is not mere coincidence that successful businessmen—men accustomed to self-reliance—make good pilots.

Contact air navigation is not hard. A ruler with a protractor attached to it—called a plotter—is the only item of equipment you need, other than air charts, of course. The clock and compass in the plane do the rest.

You'll spend a lot of time studying the Sectional, and/or the World Aeronautical Charts put out by the Coast and Geodetic people. The information contained in these charts is amazing, and since the reverse side of every one offers all the symbols and any explanation needed for their interpretation, we won't copy it here. The Sectional is drawn eight miles to the inch, and the World Aeronautical is 16 miles to the inch. So, the Sectional is more detailed, but the WA is smaller in size and easier to handle in the plane. The Sectional covers an area of approximately 150 by 285 miles, the World Aeronautical, an area of 285 by 400 miles.

Each of these charts is drawn so that a straight line on them is a Great Circle Course—the shortest distance over the surface of a globe. Ground-contour lines on air charts are in brown ink and list elevations at five-hundred-foot intervals. There is also a color code to indicate terrain height above sea level. The general elevation as shown on the chart will range from green at sea level through successively darker shades of brown as ground-surface altitude increases.

You notice too that beneath the name of each airport is a code. It tells the facilities available. For example, Downtown Airpark in Oklahoma City shows this coded information: 1180 L H 34. This means that the field elevation is 1,180 feet above sea level, there are lighted runways, hard surface, and the longest is 3,400 feet in length.

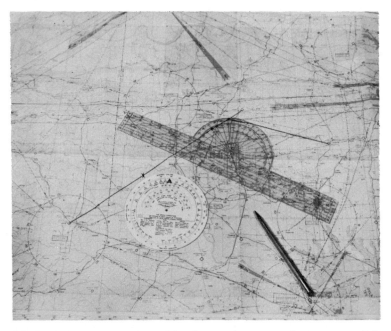

36. Navigational tools: Air chart, plotter, and computer. Directions for using the "confuser" are printed on its face.

Air charts are obtainable at all airports. They cost a quarter—one of the biggest bargains you'll ever get.

Meridians and Parallels:

You are probably familiar with the imaginary lines around the earth which navigators use in order that position, direction, and distance may be measured. The parallel lines which start at the Equator and are equidistant up to the North Pole and down to the South Pole are called the parallels of latitude. These determine points on the globe in a north-south direction.

The meridians are the lines which run from one pole to the other. That is, they converge at the poles, though they are a good distance apart at the Equator. These are used to measure east-west direction.

The meridian which passes through Greenwich, England, is the Prime or Zero Meridian. Anything west of it, around to the 180th Meridian (the half-way point), is west longitude. Everything the other way, to the 180th, is east longitude.

OBTAINING A COURSE:

True Course is the direction, measured in degrees, in which your destination lies. Imagine yourself facing north and standing in the center of a circle which is marked-off around its rim in 360 equal parts. If zero is north, then 90° will be east; 180°, south; and 270° will be west.

In the photo below, we are determining a True Course. We are using the Oklahoma City Sectional. (It takes about eighty-seven or eighty-eight Sectionals to cover the United States, and they are identified according to the names of principal cities they include.) We have drawn a line from Childress Airport to Cordell Airport. For this illustration we'll assume that we're in Childress, Texas, and our destination is Cordell, Oklahoma.

After drawing the True Course line, our second step is to find the *mid-meridian* between us and our destination. O.K., that's easy. You'll notice there are three meridians between us and Cordell, and the one nearest halfway is the one we want.

Next, we place our plotter over the True Course, with the little hole in the protractor exactly on the point where

37. (*page 69, above*) TRUE COURSE: Draw line on chart between point of departure and destination, connecting airport symbols. A straight line on an air chart is a Great Circle Course—the shortest distance between two points on a globe. 38. (*below*) OBTAINING COURSE: Protractor hole positioned at intersection of True Course line and mid-meridian, with plotter's straightedge lying along mid-meridian. True Course is then determined from protractor's edge.

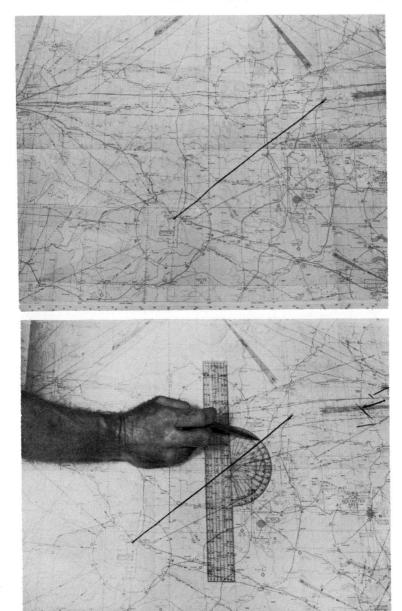

the True Course line crosses the mid-meridian. The photo of step 2 shows us pointing to the scale on the plotter's edge where the True Course is registered in degrees. In this case it is 052°.

WIND CORRECTION ANGLE:

Once an airplane is airborne, it will be carried along in the same direction as the air mass which supports it. It will fly *through* the air at its regular speed, but it will be carried with the air too, just as a boat will be carried with the current, independent of its speed through the water. And just as a boat must point its nose to one side of its intended destination in order to compensate for sidewise drift, so must an airplane.

If the wind direction and velocity are known, it's easy to establish the proper amount of correction necessary to follow a given course. It is computed by means of the *wind vector,* and works like this:

a) Draw a vertical line on a blank sheet of paper. Mark it "N" at top, "S" at bottom. It represents your mid-meridian.

b) Place the center-hole of your plotter on this line, and turn the plotter until your True Course of 052° lines up with the vertical line. (Photo 39) Then, reproduce your True Course line from the meridian along the bottom of the plotter as shown. This line is indefinite in length, but in direction corresponds with the TC line determined from your chart.

c) Now for the wind. Let's say it's from 330°, with a velocity of 30 mph. Line-up the plotter again, with the center-hole at the point where the TC line crosses the meridian, and (using the inside scale for this half of the compass) draw a line representing the wind.

The wind vector is a scale drawing from this point, and your most convenient scale is along the bottom of your

39. WIND VECTOR: Mid-meridian and True Course lines are reproduced on blank sheet of paper.

plotter. You can use these values as they are marked, or, in order to keep your diagram down in size, can mentally double these figures.

In figure 40, we're measuring 30 miles of wind along the

wind line, starting at the interception point of the three lines, in the direction the wind is *going*. Since we're doubling the scale values, that'll be 15 miles on the bottom of the plotter.

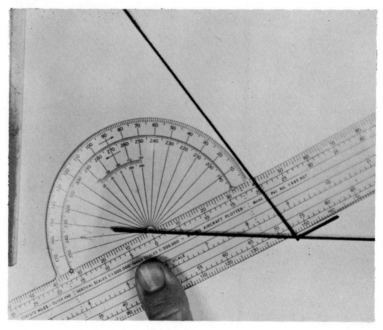

40. WIND VECTOR, step two: Adding the wind from 330 degrees.

d) The final step is to intercept the TC line with a line drawn from the end of the measured wind line. The length of this line will be our cruising air speed. Let's call it 125 mph for our plane. (Now you can see why it's handier to double the scale values: The scale we've used will be 62½ miles and will give us a more compact figure to draw.)

The completed Vector appears in fig. 41, and here's what we have: The line W-P is our air speed. Line E-D is our *track*, or the course we wish to follow. So, if we'll take our

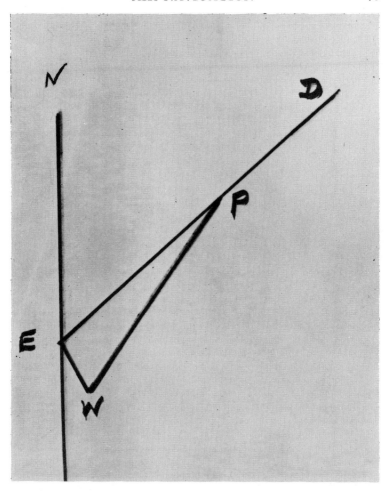

41. WIND VECTOR, step three: Add line W–P. The length of this line is determined by your plane's airspeed. Now your diagram is complete.

plotter and measure the angle at P (fig. 42), we'll find the amount of correction necessary for wind. Measuring the line E-P will give us our *ground speed*.

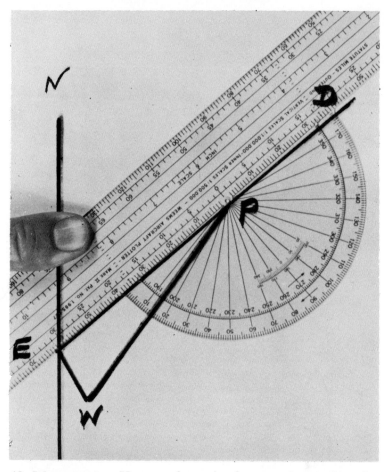

42. WIND VECTOR: Here we determine how much to correct for the wind (about 014 degrees). If we measure line E—M, we'll have our Ground Speed.

We have stretched out this process in explanation, but actually we've only drawn four lines. With a little practice you'll do a wind vector in seconds.

Referring to fig. 42, you can see that our wind correction angle is 014° and our ground speed is actually 118 mph.

The wind correction angle is always applied to our True Course according to this rule: *Add right—Subtract left.* This means that if the wind is from our right, add 014° to our TC; if from the left, subtract it. All right. In this case a glance at our vector clearly shows it to be from our left. We subtract it, and this leaves us with our *True Heading.* It is 038°. In other words, we'll point our plane's nose at 038° in order to follow a track of 052°, because of the wind.

VARIATION AND DEVIATION:

Now don't go away; there are a couple more corrections to be made before we'll arrive at the figure we'll actually follow on the magnetic compass.

We take the first one off the top of our Sectional chart. It's called *variation,* and it is the difference between true north and the magnetic pole which attracts the compass. The chart shows the area between Childress and Cordell to have a magnetic variation of 10° east.

And here's your other navigational rule: *Add west—Subtract east.*

Since our variation is given as 10° *east,* we'll subtract it from our True Heading. The result will be our *magnetic heading,* and it is 028°.

Finally, we correct for *deviation.* Deviation is error in the compass itself and is caused by radio equipment or other disturbing forces in the airplane. This figure is different for each airplane installation and is always listed on a little card near the compass or on the instrument panel.

In the plane we are using for this flight, the compass deviation card notes a minus 002° error for a magnetic heading of 028°. We'll subtract this too.

Our final figure is 026°. This is our *compass heading.* It is the actual reading we want to see on our compass in order to make good a track of 052°.

Here's a recap of the steps:

a)	Start with	True Course	052
b)	Apply	WCA	−014
	Result	True Heading	038
c)	Apply	*Variation*	−010
	Result	Magnetic Heading	028
d)	Apply	*Deviation*	−002
	Final result. . .	Compass Heading	026

Remember the two rules: For *variation,* add west and subtract east. For wind, add right and subtract left.

The magnetic compass will oscillate considerably in rough air, and after a turn, it requires a minute or so to steady down. Therefore, it can't be used during a turn as a reference in changing your heading.

MAINTAINING COURSE:

In addition to the heading we are to fly, our wind vector also gave us our ground speed. As we mentioned before, our plane always flies at the same speed *through the air* regardless of wind; but once we are airborne, we are contained within the mass of air which supports us—like a submarine below the surface—and if that mass of air is moving, we are carried with it. For this reason, the speed we are making over the ground is not the same as airspeed unless there is no wind.

Having determined ground speed, we'll measure the distance between Childress and Cordell on the chart, thus finding the time required for the flight.

The two outside scales on our plotter-ruler are for World Aeronautical Charts. The two inner scales are for Sectionals. We're using a Sectional, so, taking the figure off the inside scale (fig. 43), we find the distance to be 95 miles.

A total distance of 95 miles at a ground speed of 118 mph will mean 95 divided by 118. The result is .80, or 8/10ths of

43. MEASURING DISTANCE: Here we determine that it is 95 miles between our point of departure and our destination.

an hour. And .8 multiplied by 60 minutes tells us the flight will take 48 minutes. We'll add a little to this for climb and let-down, depending upon the extent of each.

Next, we'll establish our *check points*. These serve the same purpose for flyers that numbered highway signs do for motorists. We'd like to have one often—not more than 10 or 15 minutes apart, because the "highway" we are following is invisible—and we select them by referring to the True Course Line on our chart.

The chart shows that, 13 miles out of Childress, our track takes us across the Red River. However, we will not choose this as a check point for two reasons: It is so close—only 6½ minutes from take-off; and rivers crossed at approximate right angles are unreliable check points. We could be off

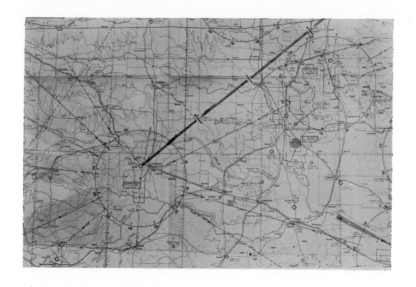

44. (*above*) CHECK POINTS: Choice of check points is up to you, but they should be not more than ten or fifteen minutes apart.
45. (*below*) ORIENTATION ON COURSE: We have just taken off from Childress Airport on our flight to Cordell. Referring to our chart (fig. 44) we note that we will cross a railroad which loops westward briefly, then angles back to parallel a highway running northward toward the river. Can you identify these? The town of Childress is out of the picture to the right.

46. (*above*) ON COURSE: Here is how the small town of Hollis appears as it comes up in the distance ahead of the nose. 47. (*below*) SECOND CHECK POINT: We have just crossed the highway, and Mangum is right out there under our wingtip to pinpoint us. Refer to fig. 44 again and see if you can spot other features shown on the air chart.

course to the right or left without knowing it, since one bend in a river looks much like another from the air.

So, for our first check point, we'll choose the town of Hollis. Our track passes directly over it, and towns don't meander across the countryside. The mileage scale on our plotter shows Hollis to be 27 miles from our departure point. At 118 mph ground speed, that is about 14 minutes flying time.

We'll fly over the Salt Fork of the Red River farther along, but we'll not use it as a principal check point. Let's pick, instead, the spot where our track crosses the highway west of the town of Mangum. Usually, crossing roads at right angles is of doubtful value as check points just as rivers are; but in this case we've got Mangum there under our right wingtip, just 5 miles away, to pinpoint us.

We'll select the town of Sentinel for our last check point because it too lies directly in our path. At the north edge of Sentinel on the chart, you'll notice an inverted triangle with a dot in its center. That will be a tall smokestack or a transmission tower. Its height above sea level is printed just above the symbol. It is labeled 1,850. Well, since the terrain beneath us is about 1,500 feet above sea level, we'll expect to find a tower there at least 350 feet high—a very satisfactory check point which is visible for some distance.

Picking your check points is up to you. Another pilot, plotting this same trip, might make different choices.

Here's a helpful tip. Look at the chart again and note that we have marked our check points with a straight line at right angles to our course. This line was carefully measured with our plotter scale. It is 4 miles long—2 miles on either side of our track. This is often handy in computing error if you should arrive over your check point slightly off course.

Also, some pilots mark the time due over each check point on the chart.

Now, another word about computers: We mentioned that

they were handy for correcting the readings of your altimeter and airspeed indicator. In addition, they will find rate-time-distance for you and eliminate the mental arithmetic we have employed in these examples.

The reverse side of some computers—the popular Dalton E6B, for example—will determine wind correction angle, thus allowing you to do away with the necessity of drawing a wind vector. However, in order to get the best use of your computer, you should fully understand the wind vector, because then you are not likely to correct for a wind from the wrong direction. In other words, having mastered the wind diagram, you will have a clearer conception of the information the computer is giving you, and you will be less likely to misread or wrongly interpret it. After all, computers are not referred to as "confusers" for no reason.

ALTERNATE AIRPORT:

Occasionally, as a form of insurance, you may decide to turn away from your intended destination (due to deteriorating weather, for example) and go to an alternate airport. And during the check-ride for your license, the FAA safety agent will require you to demonstrate your ability to do this.

Let's assume that the Childress-Cordell flight is such a check-ride and that the agent suddenly told us 5 minutes after we'd passed the check point at Sentinel that we should turn here and go to Anadarko. (He might just simply say that "conditions" have made it impossible for you to continue to Cordell, and leave it up to you to choose an alternate or, lacking a reasonable one, make a 180° turn and go back. This assumes that the weather is still good behind you. If it isn't, you have no choice but to seek an alternate; and this is why choice of an alternate is desirable before take-off.)

We have been directed to Anadarko as an alternate. Out comes the Sectional again, and the first thing we'll do is pin-

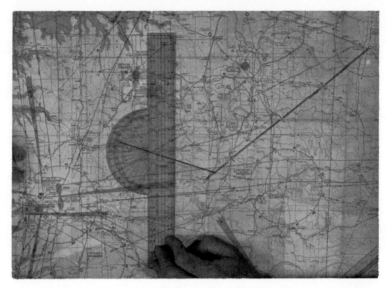

48. ALTERNATE AIRPORT: Here we are determining alternate course to Anadarko Airport.

point ourselves on the chart. Our ground speed is established at 118 mph. For all practical purposes we may call this 2 miles per minute. This puts us about 10 miles past our last check point. This is our new point of departure.

Draw a line on the chart from this point to the Anadarko Airport symbol. This is our new True Course. It measures 110°. Now, do a new wind vector.

In actual practice, you'll find it difficult to work a vector problem while flying. Therefore, when turning onto an alternate heading, it's usually best to estimate the wind correction angle and mentally add or subtract it. Mentally apply variation and deviation too. This is especially so if the weather actually is going sour, because your attention is needed outside the plane. Even drawing a new TC line on your chart can be a problem in rough air, so a helpful tip here is to fold the chart and make a sharp crease which will serve as a means of getting your new True Course.

If our wind was accurately forecast, then we've hit all our check points on the nose. Often it isn't. Therefore, let's say that we hit our last check point a couple of miles west of where we should have been—in other words, we were correcting for more wind than there actually was. Accordingly, we cut down our original, 014° wind correction angle to about 010°. This resulted in a change in our compass heading: from 026° to 030°.

Turning onto our new track and taking into account the drop in wind velocity, we'll do the new vector with a wind of about 25 mph, instead of the 30-mile wind we used for the Childress-Cordell Vector.

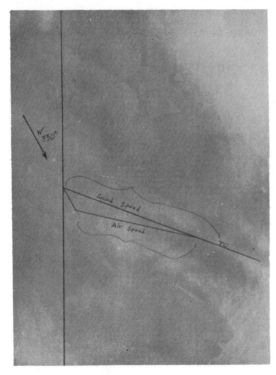

49. ALTERNATE VECTOR: Here is how our vector looks for the alternate.

This diagram shows a wind correction angle of 008°. It also tells us that—going in this direction—we'll make good a ground speed of 142 mph.

We're still in an area of 010° easterly variation, but our compass deviation card says that for a heading of 092° (TC 110, —008 WCA, —010 Variation), steer 088°. Compass heading to alternate then is 088°.

The plotter scale shows it to be 45 miles to alternate. At a ground speed of 142 mph, that is equal to 19 minutes. So, our ETA (Estimated Time of Arrival) is easy to figure, either by computer or by mental arithmetic.

Of prime importance in selecting an alternate field is the fuel supply you have available. If you have been in the air for a while before you decide to go to another destination, then your choice might be pretty limited.

At cruising speed, our plane burns nine gallons of gas per hour. She carries 18 gallons of fuel in each wing tank, which is a 4-hour supply; but for safety's sake, we always keep 45 minutes of gas in reserve, and assume in all our flight planning that she has only 3 hours and 15 minutes of gas to spend.

If this seems like a large amount of gas to burn in an hour, remember that you're cruising at 125 mph (often faster). You're traveling directly to your destination, with no curves, Sunday drivers, or stop lights; and trip for trip, your lightplane will operate less expensively than your automobile.

TOWER TALK:

To give you the clearest idea of what goes on between you and the control tower people, we'll take another "for instance." Say we're taking off from Wichita Falls and going to Lawton. After we start the engine and are ready to leave, but *before* moving the airplane, we call the tower (on 122.5 megacycles) and the conversation goes like this:

US: "Tower, this is Tri-Pacer, nine-seven-three-nine-delta. At hangar one, ready to taxi. VFR to Lawton, over."

50. CONTROL ZONE: The airspace in the vicinity of an airport, and the airport itself, are controlled by the men in the tower.

(Our airplane license number is 9739D, and "over" means that a reply is expected.)

TOWER: "Tri-Pacer, nine-seven-three-nine-delta, you are cleared to runway three-six. Wind north nine. Altimeter two-nine-nine-seven. Time one-four-five-eight. Hold west of the runway, over."

(He told us that we would use runway pointing 360°. Runways are numbered according to their compass bearing, minus their last digit. The wind is from the north at 9 mph. Our altimeter setting is 29.97. The time is 14:58, or 2:58 P.M. He also said to stop on the taxi strip and wait just off the runway.)

We will acknowledge with a "Roger." Then, after we've taxied to the position indicated, made our pre-take-off check, and are ready to go, we'll call him again.

US: "Tower, from Pacer three-nine-delta. I'm ready for take-off. Over."

TOWER: "Pacer, three-nine-delta, cleared for take-off."

That's all there is to it. Just keep it brief and simple. Also, guard tower frequency until you are out of the control zone. Almost all tower people are nice, but they don't have time to chat. On the other hand, don't hesitate to call them just because you are not up on the recommended phraseology. They understand English, and must be in contact with you for safety's sake. (We have heard of pilots faking radio trouble because they were afraid of saying the wrong thing and appearing ridiculous.)

A few miles out of Lawton, we'll call the Lawton Tower, identify ourselves, and give them our approximate position and altitude.

US: "Lawton Tower, this is Tri-Pacer nine-seven-three-nine-delta. Five miles west of Geronimo at twenty-five hundred. Landing Lawton, over."

TOWER: "Pacer three-nine-delta, this is Lawton Tower. You are cleared to enter traffic pattern. Use runway three. Wind northeast seven. Altimeter three-zero-zero-five, over."

US: "Lawton Tower, from Pacer three-nine-delta, Roger."

We will enter the traffic pattern at 800 feet, and then will receive clearance to land if there are no other planes immediately ahead of us. At large airports, we can expect to be directed to the proper taxi strip after landing.

LIGHT SIGNALS:

There are still a lot of lightplanes not equipped with two-way radio. Because of this and because radios can fail, tower operators keep a light-gun handy for directing traffic signals to planes they can't converse with. Here are the signals and their meanings. (A helpful practice: Some pilots paste these on the bottom visor of their caps or on the plane's instrument

panel, along with radio frequencies and the phonetic radio-
telephone alphabet.)

Before Take-off:

Steady red—Stop taxiing and hold position.
Flashing red—Taxi clear of landing area.
Steady green—Cleared for take-off.
Flashing green—Clear to continue taxiing.
Alternate red & green—Caution.
White—Return to flight line.

Before Landing:

Steady red—Hold position in pattern, continue to circle.
Flashing red—Airport unsafe; do not land.
Steady green—Cleared to land.
Flashing green—Return and land.
Alternate red & green—Caution.

At night, acknowledge these signals by blinking your landing lights.

A large white "X" displayed on a field means the field is
closed. And we'll repeat that a flashing amber light atop the
control tower indicates a right-hand pattern. This may also
be shown by a right-angled marker on the field.

CRUISING ALTITUDES:

VFR (Visual Flight Rules) cross-country flights must be
made at the following altitudes as measured above sea level:

Any easterly magnetic heading from and including due
north to 179°, fly at *odd thousands plus 500 feet.*

Any westerly magnetic heading from and including due
south to 359°, fly at *even thousands plus 500 feet.*

These legal altitudes begin at 3,000 feet above the *surface.*

RADIO AIDS TO NAVIGATION:

There are two kinds of radio beams that you may follow to your destination. First, let's consider the old low-frequency beams. They have guided U.S. aircraft for over twenty-five years. About a hundred are still in operation.

The LF Range sends out a beam in four directions. The transmission of its signals are so arranged as to send out a Morse Code "A" (dit-dah) to define one edge of the beam, and a Morse Code "N" (dah-dit) to define the other edge. These merge in the center of the beam to a high-pitched hum.

When tracking on an LF Beam, you should keep to the center where neither letter predominates. (This is a new rule. Prior to adoption of the new altitude separation rule, you were required to keep to the right, where one letter of the signal was predominant.) On your chart, these beams are shown in dark red ink, and the "N" quadrant is identified by a solid line.

To insure that you are following the proper beam, listen for the beam's three-letter identification in Morse Code, which is broadcast every thirty seconds. (This three-letter identification is printed in red ink in a "box" near the station on your chart.) And to be sure that you are flying toward, rather than away from, the station, check your map for the side of the beam where "N" predominates. Of course, the signal will finally fade as you fly away from it; its range is normally about 50 to 100 miles.

As you approach the ground transmitting station of an LF Beam, it will grow louder and you must turn down your volume frequently. Passing directly over the station you will be in the *cone of silence* for a minute or so (depending upon your altitude and speed), then as you enter the opposite side, the signal will surge back stronger than ever.

The Airway Weathercasts are given on this frequency at 15 minutes after the hour, and 15 minutes before the hour around the clock. The first is a local report; the other, general.

Now about *Omni*. Forgive us while we say, "Omni, it's wonderful!" It is, too. In the first place, the Omnirange signal is VHF—very high frequency, like TV or Radar—and therefore almost completely free of static. There are about 400 Omnirange Stations throughout the U.S. now, and they'll take you almost anywhere.

As the name suggests, an Omni Station sends out signals in *all* directions, instead of only four. Regardless of where you are or where you want to go, Omni (also called VOR, for Very High Frequency Omnirange System) will take you there.

Your Omni receiver in your plane employs three instruments: *bearing selector, deviation indicator,* and the *To-From indicator.*

The *bearing selector* is a dial containing the points of the compass on its face, with a needle which you manually set to the magnetic bearing you wish to fly.

The *deviation indicator* shows any deviation from your course. As long as the needle is centered, you are flying directly on your preset track. That's all there is to it: Fly the needle. Keep it centered, and you'll arrive at your destination.

The *To-From indicator* has a needle which points to one of these two legends. It tells you whether you are approaching, or going away from, the station to which you are tuned.

Let's again take an example. Let's say the flight we made from Childress to Cordell was by Omni Navigation. Referring to the chart, note that the Childress Omni Station is due south of the airport. It is that little ring with the dot in the center, and it is in the middle of the Omni compass rose, the big circle which is marked off in degrees.

We'll draw our TC Line from that point to Cordell. (Cordell has no Omni, you will note.) On the edge of the compass rose, we'll see that our Magnetic Heading is 040°.

We'll take off, set the *bearing selector* on 040°, and tune in Childress Radio. Then, we'll fly east—about 4 miles—until we intercept the radial. When we do intercept it, our *deviation indicator* will come to life. So, we'll turn in that direction to keep the needle centered. From here on, as long as we are on course, the needle will remain centered. The *To-From* needle will point to "From."

If there is a cross-wind, we will discover that holding 040° (plus or minus compass deviation) on the magnetic compass will not keep the *deviation indicator's* needle centered. Nevertheless, *center the needle*. If you find that you must steer five, ten, or even more degrees to either side of 040 on the magnetic compass in order to keep the needle centered, do it. Because the difference between 040 and whatever it takes to keep the needle centered, is simply your wind correction angle. So, we'll repeat: As long as that needle is centered, you're following the heading you set on the *bearing selector*.

Now, let's plan a longer flight using Omni. Let's make Oklahoma City our destination. Referring to the chart, you can see that, after taking off from Childress Airport, the Omni radial we want to follow (053°) lies 8 or 9 miles east. Well, tune in Childress Radio, set the *bearing selector* on 053, and as soon as we intercept the 053° radial, our *deviation indicator* needle will inform us. Turn toward our destination and, from here on, keep the needle centered. The *To-From* needle will show "From." How simple can navigation get?

About halfway to the Hobart Omni, we can tune it in in place of the Childress Omni we've been using. Now our *To-From* needle will swing to "To."

As we pass over the Hobart Omni Station, the *deviation* needle will hunt back and forth and the *To-From* needle will, of course, as the station passes behind, swing to "From." At this point, however, the chart shows that we must change heading slightly and follow the 051 radial from here to Oke

City. O.K. Reset the *bearing selector* to 051 and ease the nose very slightly to the left to keep the needle centered on the *deviation indicator*. Later, approaching Oke City, we can switch to Oke City Omni.

In keeping your *deviation* needle centered, "follow it with the plane"; in other words, if it is off to the right, turn right to bring it back. It's best to make small corrections.

O.K., so you want to know why, if flying Omni is so easy, we spent so much time messing around with wind vectors, check points, and stuff. Well, there are several good answers: In the first place, radios can fail. Secondly, an Omni receiver for your plane is costly. Probably less than half of present day lightplanes have them. Most important, however, is your degree of proficiency as a flyer. A capable pilot is a safe pilot. The pilot who becomes a slave to Omni has no margin for error, while the flyer who understands the basic principles of navigation knows that he can depend upon himself—with or without Omni's magic.

You can get a companion piece of equipment to go with your Omni receiver which practically puts you in the airliner class. This is called *DME (Distance Measuring Equipment)* and this amazing little box will keep you informed about your exact distance to or from whichever Omni Station you have tuned. It too offers its information on a dial on the instrument panel.

One final thing about Omni: You need not fly from one Omni Station to the next. If both your point of departure and your destination are without nearby Omni sites, you may use those off your course to either side by cross-tuning for frequent position checks.

All radio frequencies are printed directly on your air chart in a "box" beside each installation. Also, the *Airman's Guide,* published every two weeks, keeps you up to date on any changes and new stations.

IV
The Examination

The Examination

OBTAINING YOUR LICENSE:

Obtaining your Private "Ticket" will be an informal thing, and your training probably seemed informal. You made an appointment with your flight instructor a couple or three times a week, you learned mostly by "doing," and although there was a brief period (when you had about six or seven hours) that you couldn't seem to do anything right, your instructor had finally said one morning, "Why don't you take 'er around alone? I'd like to stretch my legs awhile."

Well, you know now there was no need for that small suspicion which hinted maybe you weren't quite ready yet. You were. Flight instructors today must pass rigid government tests, and when one turns you loose for solo, there's a lot of training and experience backing that decision.

He is also a good judge of people; and your mental attitude, as well as your flying ability, entered into his decision.

With 40 hours certified in your logbook—including 10 hours of solo cross-country time—you may request the FAA safety agent to give you your exam for a Private License. The test will consist of a written exam, and a check ride in a plane with which you are familiar.

There's not much point in advising you not to be nervous, since that's a pretty normal reaction. It might help you to remember, however, that the FAA agent is a pilot himself —a good one—and he takes no pleasure in flunking anyone.

He really won't be any more critical than your instructor. If you satisfied your instructor, you have nothing to fear from the FAA agent.

THE CHECK RIDE:

The agent will grade you on your preflight check of the airplane. He'll ask a few questions about the plane's airworthiness, and registration certificates, and he'll note your ground-operating procedures.

After take-off, the test will be in two phases. The first will concern your control of the plane and your respect for, and knowledge of, Civil Air Regulations.

The second will be a demonstration of your ability to fly a previously plotted cross-country course. (Earlier, when you plotted the course on the ground, we hope you didn't forget to get all the dope on the weather!) As mentioned before, he will probably request that you fly to an alternate field after you have shown aptitude on your original course.

He will ask for level flight, climbing and gliding turns, and stall recovery from take-off-speed climbing turns. He will also want to see cross-wind take-offs and landings. In addition, a new amendment to the C.A.R. requires that you demonstrate the ability to maintain control of your plane in case you are accidentally caught on instruments. Without visual reference to the ground, you must make a 180-degree turn and backtrack into clear weather. Section V explains this procedure in detail.

The sample written exam which follows later in this section is typical. The actual examination will have many of these same questions. The cross-country flight which you will be required to plot may be over a different section of the country, but it will be a triangular course similar to the one given here.

In taking your exam, you will be expected to make use of the current *Airman's Guide,* the *Flight Information Manual,* and the *Airplane Flight Manual* (sometimes called *Airplane Operation Manual*). Also, you may use a computer.

The *Airman's Guide* is published every two weeks. It keeps you up to date on radio frequencies, and lists pertinent data on all airports.

The *Flight Information Manual* is published yearly, and outlines Air Traffic Procedures, Search and Rescue Procedures, and Radio Procedures.

Your *Airplane Flight Manual* contains information about your plane: its load limits, fuel consumption, performance under varying conditions, and its landing and take-off requirements.

In addition to the above, the agent will issue to you a *Sectional Chart* and a complete mythical *Weather Report*. You will use these in planning the cross-country flight given in the written portion of the examination.

In practice, you could get the weather by going to the weather office (if there is one at your field) and studying the weather map and/or reading the hourly sequence reports as they come in by teletype. Or, you could telephone and ask for it, or you could rely on the radio broadcast which comes over the LF Radio at 15 minutes after the hour and 15 minutes before the hour.

The test will employ an hourly sequence report from the teletype.

The mythical cross-country flight contained in the written exam is defined as a triangular course: Lawton, Oklahoma, to Amarillo, Texas, via Hobart Omni; refuel at Amarillo, and fly to Childress, Texas, thence back to Lawton.

So, you will get your local Aviation Weather Forecast, and the Amarillo sequence report. Following, is what came off the wire from Amarillo:

AMA 0 15 245 /82/51/ ↗10/ 003

Decoded it means: Amarillo, clear, 15 miles visibility, sea level pressure 1024.5 millibars, temperature 82, dew point

51, wind SW 10 knots, altimeter setting 30.03.

When cloud cover and ceiling are given, they are expressed in hundreds of feet. The first digit is omitted from the altimeter setting along with the decimal.

Winds Aloft Forecasts also are obtained from the teletype. Their velocities are given in knots. Converting knots to mph, multiply by 1.15, or take the conversion from your computer.

The Winds Aloft sequence runs like this:

AMA 09 02615 42620 2724 62830 2932

Left to right it reads: Amarillo, 9 A.M. Greenwich Civil Time. Surface wind is from 260° with a velocity of 15 knots. (The surface wind is not given in some Winds Aloft reports.) At 4,000 feet wind is from 260° at 20 knots; at 5,000 feet wind is from 270° at 24 knots (altitude is not listed for odd-thousands). At 6,000 feet wind is from 280° at 30 knots, etc. Note that Amarillo's Winds Aloft report began at 4,000 feet. This is because Amarillo is approximately 3,600 feet above sea level, and winds aloft altitudes are measured, not above ground, but above sea level.

Aviation Forecasts are also received by teletype. They are written in two parts, Regional and Terminal (local). They are made up every 6 hours to cover a forecast period of 12 hours.

Pictured below is the flight you will plot for the exam which follows. You'll use the Oklahoma City Sectional Chart and plan the flight for the Pacer, three-nine-delta. You know that Three-nine-delta cruises at 125 mph IAS (Indicated Air Speed) and that she carries a total of 36 gallons of gas. Take-off time is given as 09:15.

The exam follows.

CIVIL AIR REGULATIONS

1. An alternating red and green control light from the tower, either on the ground or in the air, means:

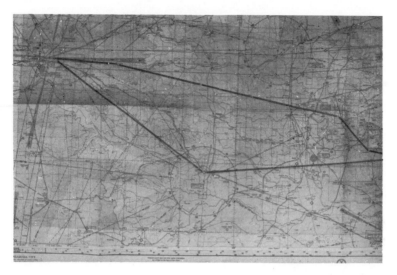

51. EXAM, CROSS-COUNTRY: You will plot this flight from Lawton Airport to Indiahoma by pilotage, then to Hobart OMNI via OMNI signal. Follow OMNI signal to Groom, Texas, then by pilotage fly direct to Amarillo Airport and refuel. The leg from Amarillo Airport to Childress Airport is also by pilotage. Turn over Childress and return to Lawton Airport.

    a. Exercise caution.
    b. You are second to land (or take-off).
    c. For airliners only.
    d. There is no such signal.

2. As you prepare to start your take-off run, you receive a flashing red light from the tower. It means:

    a. Get out and check for fire.
    b. Stay where you are.
    c. Return to hangar.
    d. Taxi clear of landing area or runway.

3. When flying VFR outside of control zones and control areas, minimum visibility is:

    a. 3 miles.
    b. 1 mile.
    c. To be able to see ground below.
    d. 500 feet.

4. Flying cross-country on a magnetic heading of 015° and more than 3,000 feet above the surface, you must fly at:

    a. Even thousands plus 500 feet.
    b. Odd thousands plus 500 feet.
    c. Even thousands.
    d. Odd thousands.

5. A flashing amber light on the control tower means:

    a. Caution.
    b. Field is closed.
    c. Right-hand traffic pattern in use.
    d. Hold your position until further notice.

6. If you receive a steady red light while in the traffic pattern, you should:

    a. Give way to other traffic and continue circling.
    b. Check landing gear; you've forgotten to put the wheels down.
    c. Go to alternate airport; field is closed.
    d. Fly clear of traffic pattern; emergency exists.

7. Your Private Pilot's Medical Certificate must be renewed:

    a. Yearly.
    b. Only in case of accident.
    c. Every 24 months.
    d. Every 6 months.

8. Responsibility for closing a flight plan rests with:

    a. Airport manager at your destination.

    b. Control tower operator.

    c. Is closed automatically when you reach destination.

    d. Pilot in command (You).

9. When two airplanes are approaching head-on:

    a. The slower should pass under, the faster, over.

    b. The highest plane always has the right-of-way.

    c. Both shall slow down and give way to the left.

    d. Each must give way to the right, passing not closer than 500 feet.

10. Aircraft registration and airworthiness certificates should be kept:

    a. In a safe place.

    b. On your person at all times when flying.

    c. In the plane.

    d. On file in the office at your home field.

11. Filing of a flight plan is mandatory:

    a. When carrying passengers.

    b. For all IFR flights.

    c. Only for planes of 300 hp or more.

    d. For all cross-country flights.

12. Upon demand, you must show your license and current medical certificate to:

    a. Any authorized law enforcement officer.

    b. Only to FAA safety agents.

    c. Safety agents and airport managers only.

    d. Safety agents, tower personnel, and flight instructors only.

WEATHER RECOGNITION

13. Winds around a high-pressure area blow:

    a. Counterclockwise and inward.

    b. Clockwise and outward.

    c. Clockwise and inward.

    d. Counterclockwise and outward.

14. Generally, weather and pressure areas move across the United States from:

    a. West to east.

    b. East to west.

    c. North to south.

    d. South to north.

15. In winter, an air mass forming in north-central Canada and moving south across the United States would be a:

    a. Maritime polar.

    b. Polar continental.

    c. Cool front.

    d. Squall line.

16. Fog or precipitation may be expected when:

    a. Dew point and temperature are 10 degrees apart.

    b. Dew point and temperature are close together and spread between them is decreasing.

    c. Spread between them is increasing.

    d. When wind is less than 5 mph with low clouds.

17. Which of the following takes place after a cold front has passed?

    a. Increase in pressure.

    b. Bumpy air.

    c. Pronounced wind shift.

    d. All of the above.

18. Isobars located close together on a weather map mean:

    a. Rain.

    b. Low wind velocities.

   c. High wind velocities.

   d. Small map.

19. A squall line is a line of heavy thunderstorms. It sometimes runs a few miles ahead of:

   a. A cold front.

   b. A warm front.

   c. An occluded front.

   d. A stationary front.

20. As a general rule when approaching a thunderstorm on a cross-country flight, you should:

   a. Climb above it.

   b. Avoid it completely, landing if necessary in order to stay clear of the winds near it.

   c. Fly through at about 6,000 feet where there is a minimum of turbulence.

   d. Fly under so that ground contact won't be lost.

21. On the downwind sides of mountain ranges, there may be:

   a. Updrafts.

   b. Still, heavy air causing your altimeter to read lower than is correct.

   c. Bumpy air causing your altimeter to fluctuate.

   d. Downdrafts, causing your altimeter to register higher than is correct.

22. Flying cross-country, you should call the tower several miles before reaching your destination. Acknowledging your call, he will give you, among other things, an altimeter setting. He does this because:

   a. It gives you a chance to check the accuracy of the instrument.

   b. To make you feel welcome.

    c. Because natural barometric pressure varies from place to place, and you must correct your instrument for local conditions to get an accurate reading.

    d. The law requires it.

23. In the lower atmosphere (below 20,000 feet) under normal conditions, temperature of the air decreases:

    a. 2% per thousand feet of altitude.

    b. About 3½ degrees per thousand feet of altitude.

    c. An amount which depends upon time of year.

    d. No definite relation between altitude and temp.

24. High and Low Pressure areas are weather makers. If your destination on a cross-country flight is within a well-defined High, you can expect weather there to:

    a. Be generally clear, with good flying conditions.

    b. Be stormy.

    c. Be uncertain; stormy weather on the way.

    d. Depend upon whether wind is circulating clockwise, or counterclockwise.

25. Winds Aloft Reports are important in planning a cross-country flight. Their velocities are given:

    a. In miles per hour.

    b. In knots.

    c. By designation: moderate, strong, or hurricane.

    d. Small, medium, or large.

The following questions pertain to aircraft operation and cross-country flying and navigation techniques. In answering some of these questions, a simple flight log will be helpful. Most pilots use one similar to that pictured below.

26. Your Pacer, Three-nine-delta, is equipped with two-way VHF Radio, and an LF receiver. Preparing to take off, your first radio contact with the tower will be:

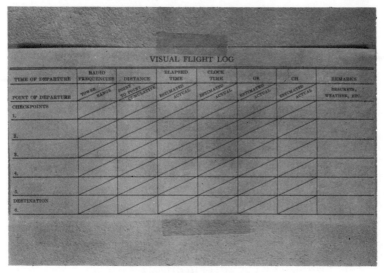

52. FLIGHT LOG.

    a. When you request take-off clearance.
    b. While taxiing to the runway.
    c. To request taxi instructions after starting the engine.
    d. Before preflight inspection of the plane.

27. During the first half-minute of engine operation, the most important thing to check is:

    a. Loss of rpm.
    b. Oil pressure.
    c. To be sure that you have plenty of whiskey along.
    d. The traffic pattern for incoming planes.

28. The fuel-strainer sediment-bowl should be drained:

    a. By the pilot before each flight.
    b. Every ten hours of flight; it is the mechanic's responsibility.

   c. Airplanes don't have fuel strainers.
   d. Once weekly, whether plane is flown or not.

29. In plotting your course, variation should be computed according to this rule:

   a. Add west, subtract east.
   b. Add east, subtract west.
   c. Add right, subtract left.
   d. Add 2% per thousand feet.

30. You used a Sectional Air Chart in planning your flight because it is more detailed than the smaller World Aeronautical Chart. Both, however, indicate general elevation of the ground by:

   a. Color.
   b. Listing it on margin of maps.
   c. Not given; your altimeter shows you this.
   d. Information printed in a "box" near each airport symbol.

According to the *Airplane Operation Manual* for the Three-nine-delta, she weighs 1,114 lbs. empty and has a maximum gross limit of 2,000 lbs. Therefore, she will lift 886 lbs. in addition to her own weight. You must subtract 15 lbs. for oil. This leaves 871 lbs. to spread between passengers, baggage, and fuel.

Now remember in figuring your fuel for a given flight always to keep a safe margin for emergency. We recommend a reserve equal to 45 minutes of flying time which is, in the Pacer, 7 gallons. Also remember—because from now on you'll need to constantly—that gasoline weighs about 6 lbs. per gallon.

With this information at hand, let's continue with the exam:

31. If you were taking three people with you on this flight,

making a total of four, and weighing 680 lbs., and each of you have 20 lbs. of baggage, you can carry:

a. 18½ gallons of fuel.
b. 23½ gallons of fuel.
c. 36 gallons of fuel.
d. 28½ gallons of fuel.

32. What is the maximum distance you could fly on this amount of gas, assuming no wind condition and keeping your 7-gallon reserve intact?

a. Approximately 160 miles.
b. About 210 miles.
c. About 320 miles.
d. About 107 miles.

33. If your weight is 170 lbs., and you are taking off alone with full tanks, you are below your allowable maximum by:

a. 485 lbs.
b. 385 lbs.
c. 285 lbs.
d. 185 lbs.

34. To determine True Course, you should:

a. Measure the magnetic bearing of your destination.
b. Construct a wind vector.
c. Take it from your computer.
d. Draw line on your air chart and measure the angle from the mid-meridian.

35. Tower, LF Radio, and Omni frequencies are:

a. Listed on reverse side of all air charts.
b. Printed in a "box" at each radio location on the chart.
c. Not listed on air charts; must be taken from *Airman's Guide*.

    d. All the same.

36. Approaching an airport, tower gives you an altimeter setting which you adjust on your altimeter. When your wheels touch down, your altimeter will read:

    a. Zero.

    b. Elevation above sea level at which airport is located.

    c. Zero, unless a low pressure exists.

    d. Zero, plus the distance from the ground to the instrument itself.

37. Compass deviation is caused by:

    a. Masses of metal and radio equipment in the plane; it is different for each plane.

    b. It is the difference between true north and magnetic north.

    c. Careless pilotage—it means deviating from course.

    d. The pull of magnetic north on one edge of the compass.

38. If your best climbing speed in still air is 90 mph indicated airspeed, with a 20 mph headwind it will be:

    a. 90 mph indicated.

    b. 70 mph indicated.

    c. 110 mph indicated.

    d. About 90 mph ground speed.

39. The gliding angle of a loaded airplane compared to that plane's unloaded angle is:

    a. The same.

    b. Greater.

    c. Shallower.

    d. Dependent on the wind.

40. If your gas tank vents are plugged, this will:

    a. Reduce gasoline evaporation and help fuel pump maintain better suction.

    b. Prevent moisture condensation in tank.

    c. Result in engine failure from fuel starvation.

    d. Make no difference.

41. You should "clear" your engine with the throttle during long glides because:

    a. It prevents the cylinders from loading up with gas.

    b. Decreases lift/drag ratio.

    c. It keeps the battery charged.

    d. Keeps magnetos hot and insures good ignition.

42. Approaching a large airport from the east, you are told to use runway 9. You will:

    a. Land west to east.

    b. Land east to west.

    c. Land north to south.

    d. Land slightly east of north; this stands for 9°.

43. Beneath the airport symbol at Amarillo on your Sectional are the characters, 3604 L H 60. This means:

    a. Runway is 3,604 feet long, low and high frequency radio, and field elevation is 60 feet.

    b. Field elevation is 3,604 feet, lighted and hard-surfaced runway, and longest runway is 6,000 feet.

    c. 3604 is radio frequency. LH means large hangar, and 60 is magnetic bearing of main runway.

    d. 3604 is LF identification number. LH means left-hand pattern is used, and 60 is airway number.

44. Magnetic variation is obtained:

    a. From card placed near compass in cockpit.

    b. By adding 2% per thousand feet for this.

    c. From any air chart and is shown by broken line.

d. From the plane's operation manual.

45. If your plane's airspeed indicator normally reads about 55 mph when landing at sea level, then landing at an airport 4,700 feet above sea level it will read:

   a. 45 mph.
   b. 65 mph.
   c. Same.
   d. 75 mph.

   The *Koch Chart For Altitude and Temperature Effects* is shown below, with instructions for its use. This is printed on the reverse side of Sectional Air Charts, and by referring to it, you can quickly determine the amount of additional take-off run needed for any given condition of temperature or airport elevation.

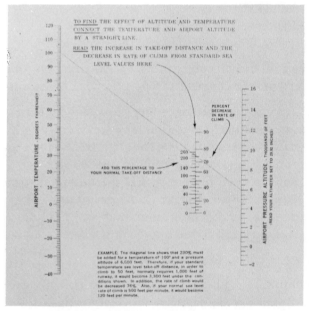

53. KOCH CHART.

Employ the chart shown above for answering the following two questions.

46. Taking off from Lawton Airport with maximum gross load, you know temperature to be 78° and the Lawton Airport 1,108 ft. elevation. You also know, by referring to your plane's Flight Operation Manual, that Three-nine-delta's normal take-off (computed at Standard Atmosphere, 59° F. at sea level) is 1,120 feet. Therefore, using the Koch Chart you know that you will need approximately for this take-off an additional:

    a. 366 ft.
    b. 166 ft.
    c. 3,660 ft.
    d. 1,660 ft.

47. If the temperature were 90° F. and you were taking off from a field of 6,000 ft. elevation, you would require an additional take-off run of approximately:

    a. 2,196 ft.
    b. 1,196 ft.
    c. 4,196 ft.
    d. The same as at sea level.

48. Although this flight will be VFR, you file a Flight Plan:

    a. To warn airliners to watch out for you.
    b. To insure that Air Search will look for you if you fail to reach your destination within a reasonable time.
    c. To allow the Ground Observer Corps to identify you.
    d. Because the law requires it.

49. In plotting your course, you established check points:

    a. About an hour apart.
    b. 10 to 15 minutes apart.
    c. Not necessary in clear weather.

54. FLIGHT PLAN.

d. On the mid-meridian.

50. Carburetor ice is most likely to be encountered:

   a. At any temperature between approximately 25° F. and 70° F.
   b. Only when the temperature is 32° or below.
   c. When you are flying through extremely cold, dry air.
   d. Ice can't form in the carburetor.

51. The first leg of your cross-country flight is from Lawton to Amarillo via Hobart Omni. You cannot fly directly to Hobart Omni, however, because of the Restricted Area lying across your normal track. Therefore, you will fly to the small town of Indiahoma, turn there, detouring around the Restricted Air Space, and pick up a "To" Omni signal from Hobart Omni. Your True Course from Lawton to Indiahoma will be:

a. 100°.
b. 280°.
c. 260°.
d. 70°.

52. You have chosen to fly at 3,500 ft. (roughly 2,000 ft. above the surface) for the first part of your trip because the Winds Aloft Report revealed increasing head winds at greater heights. At this altitude, forecast wind is from 255° at 19 knots. Converted to miles per hour, this equals approximately:

a. 27 mph.
b. 22 mph.
c. 30 mph.
d. 25 mph.

53. Not counting your reduced airspeed during climb, but assuming normal 125 mph airspeed for the short flight to Indiahoma, your wind correction angle is:

a. 004°.
b. 011°.
c. None.
d. 017°.

54. You took off at 09:15. Eleven minutes later, you are over Indiahoma. You turn northwest and tune Hobart Omni. You set your *Bearing Selector* at:

a. 340°.
b. 305°.
c. 090°.
d. 125°.

55. If the wind has been accurately forecast, you expect to arrive over Hobart Omni Station at about:

a. 09:39.

b. 09:50.

c. 09:31.

d. 09:55.

56. If the wind has been accurately forecast, your ground speed between Indiahoma and Hobart Omni is about:

a. 105 mph.

b. 135 mph.

c. 112 mph.

d. 127 mph.

57. Assuming that you arrive over Hobart Omni Station exactly on your ETA (thus confirming the wind to be as forecast) you will make a shallow left turn for the next leg to Amarillo. You will reset your Omni *bearing selector* to:

a. 285°.

b. 272°.

c. 090°.

d. 230°.

58. Your track takes you over Lake Altus, 13 miles outbound from Hobart Omni. However, from there to your next good check point, the tiny town of Dozier, it is about 60 miles. You should pass over Dozier at approximately:

a. 10:30 A.M.

b. 10:00 A.M.

c. 10:19 A.M.

d. 09:57 A.M.

59. The highest terrain over which you will fly on this trip (Lawton-Amarillo-Childress-Lawton) is shown on the chart as:

a. Between 1,000 and 2,000 ft. above sea level.

b. Between 1,500 and 2,500 ft. above sea level.

c. Between 4,000 and 4,500 ft. above sea level.

d. Slightly over 3,600 ft. above sea level.

60. During your flight westward, the terrain beneath became higher. Arriving in the vicinity of the Amarillo Airport, you see the altimeter indicates 5,650 ft. You are:

    a. Violating the altitude separation rule.
    b. Approximately 2,000 ft. above the surface, and not in violation of altitude separation rules.
    c. About 3,500 ft. above the surface; but the separation rule applies only to airliners.
    d. 5,650 ft. above the surface, because altimeters register height above surface.

61. Total distance from Lawton to Amarillo is approximately:

    a. 200 miles.
    b. 183 miles.
    c. 215 miles.
    d. 275 miles.

62. If you land at Amarillo Airport at 11:08, Three-nine-delta will require:

    a. Almost 18 gallons of fuel to refill.
    b. Nearly 30 gallons to refill.
    c. Less than 15 gallons.
    d. About 24 gallons.

63. At 12 noon, you leave Amarillo bound for Childress. You will not make use of radio aids for this leg of the flight. While on the ground at Amarillo, you checked the weather again and found the Winds Aloft Report to be the same as forecast at 09:00. By means of a wind vector or your computer, you expect your ground speed on this heading to be:

    a. 116 mph.
    b. 154 mph.
    c. 132 mph.
    d. 163 mph.

64. This being the case, you expect to arrive over Childress Airport at about:

    a. 12:50 P.M.
    b. 12:40 P.M.
    c. 12:29 P.M.
    d. 12:31 P.M.

65. Arriving over Childress Airport, you turn for your final leg of the flight. As plotted before take-off this morning, you will not make use of radio aids for the inbound flight to Lawton. Your True Course, from airport to airport, is:

    a. 075°.
    b. 085°.
    c. 095°.
    d. 091°.

66. Your altimeter now reads 4,000 ft. Assuming the Winds Aloft are remaining the same, your wind correction angle will be:

    a. 020°.
    b. 002°.
    c. 012°.
    d. none.

67. One of the check points you have chosen on this leg is Olustee Airport. It lies on the north edge of your track, about 49 miles outbound from Childress. Arriving in this vicinity, you find yourself about 4 miles south of where you should be, and 5 minutes past your estimated

time over this point. Therefore, you know that:

a. Wind is stronger than forecast, and from a more northerly direction.
b. Wind is weaker than forecast, and from a more northerly direction.
c. Wind has swung to the south and become stronger.
d. Wind has died.

68. Your Compass Heading from Childress to Lawton was 075°. To correct for this change in forecast wind, you will now:

a. Change your heading to a few degrees more than 075.
b. Change heading to few degrees less than 075.
c. Speed up and continue on 075° heading.
d. Go back to Childress and start over.

69. You reach Lawton at 1:32 and enter the traffic pattern at:

a. 500 ft. above sea level on downwind leg.
b. 800 ft. above the surface on downwind leg.
c. 45° angle on upwind leg.
d. 1,000 ft. altitude on base leg.

Note: Had Three-nine-delta not been equipped with an Omni receiver, you would have plotted this trip differently. You could simply have drawn a line on your chart between Lawton and Amarillo, picked your check points, and after getting the weather and doing your vectors, have taken-off to fly a direct course. Or, you may have continued the Indiahoma-Hobart leg northward to intercept Airway Red 24, in order to follow the LF Beam to Amarillo. (We would rather have this sample exam be tough than omit an important point covered in the actual test.)

70. Omni bearings marked on the chart are:

    a. True Courses.
    b. Magnetic bearings.
    c. Corrected for compass deviation.
    d. Corrected to sea-level pressure.

71. LF Beams are shown on the chart according to:

    a. True direction in which they point.
    b. Their magnetic headings.
    c. True direction corrected for compass deviation.
    d. They all point north-south, and east-west.

72. On air charts, the "N" quadrant of an LF Beam can be identified by:

    a. Solid red line.
    b. Dotted line.
    c. The letter "N."
    d. The fact that it is always to your right when pointing toward station.

ANSWERS TO PRIVATE PILOT'S EXAMINATION

1. a.	25. b.	49. b.
2. d.	26. c.	50. a.
3. b.	27. b.	51. b.
4. b.	28. a.	52. b.
5. c.	29. a.	53. a.
6. a.	30. a.	54. b.
7. c.	31. a.	55. a.
8. d.	32. a.	56. c.
9. d.	33. a.	57. b.
10. c.	34. d.	58. c.
11. b.	35. b.	59. d.
12. a.	36. b.	60. b.
13. b.	37. a.	61. a.

14. a.	38. a.	62. a.
15. b.	39. b.	63. b.
16. b.	40. c.	64. b.
17. d.	41. a.	65. b.
18. c.	42. a.	66. b.
19. a.	43. b.	67. b.
20. b.	44. c.	68. b.
21. d.	45. c.	69. b.
22. c.	46. a.	70. b.
23. b.	47. a.	71. b.
24. a.	48. b.	72. a.

V

Emergency Instrument Procedure

Emergency Instrument Procedure

It is possible that the time may come when you'll find yourself—purely by accident, of course—smack in the middle of instrument weather conditions. Naturally, you don't *intend* to be caught "on the gauges"; you're no aerial hotrodder, and you always check the weather before take-off. But the trouble is that weather forecasting is not yet an exact science and, well, if some of those anonymous "statistics" could speak—

Now this is not to say that every pilot should have an instrument rating. Such a thing is neither practical nor desirable. However, there are a few simple things you can learn which will, if and when you are caught in the soup, allow you to maintain positive control of your plane and get down safely. This involves the use of only two instruments—instruments with which you are already familiar.

In most cases when you are accidentally caught on instruments, clear weather will lie behind you, from where you have just come. Therefore, by simply turning around and flying a reciprocal course you will return to contact flying conditions. It's simple, but not quite as simple as it sounds.

Here's why: Once you've lost visual contact with the ground, your sense of balance and sense of direction—including your up-and-down sense—are gone. Non-flyers find this hard to believe, but it is true. Instrument instructors are familiar with the novice who, under the hood, leans far to one side, unconsciously straining against a banking condition which does not exist. The student's sense of equilibrium, when he is denied a look at the ground, falsely tells him he is banking. The instruments know better, though it takes awhile for most of us to place our trust where it is deserved—even with life at stake.

This brings up the first and, perhaps, most important rule: *Always believe your instruments.* If your turn-needle says that you are turning, then no matter what the seat-of-your-pants says, *believe the turn-needle.*

This is the central fact to be learned in controlling your plane without visual reference to the ground. Your nervous system will lie to you. Know this—and believe only the impersonal, nerveless gauges.

You will understand that in discussing the following procedure, all we are talking about is maintaining positive control of your airplane. This is not instrument flying as the pros do it, but merely sound and proven technique for the non-instrument pilot to follow in case he is inadvertently caught on instruments.

First, let's consider how most non-instrument pilots get into serious trouble after flying into instrument weather. Usually within a minute or two a wing will drop a little. This will cause the plane to start a gentle turn. (The pilot, unable to see the ground, is unaware of this for reasons we have seen.) Next, the nose will drop a little to make up for the loss of lift due to the unsuspected bank. Finally, the pilot becomes aware of the increasing airspeed, and therefore comes back on the wheel. But this has the effect of tightening the spiral because, as you know, back pressure on the wheel pulls the nose toward the pilot—increases the angle of attack—and to pull the nose toward the pilot in a spiral is to tighten the spiral, for the wings are not level. At this point then, the pilot is only seconds away from becoming a Statistic.

Sure, it's a bit gruesome maybe, but it will help you to understand the importance of your turn-needle any time you're without visual ground contact. So, keep that turn-needle centered; then a wing can't get down unnoticed to start this fatal pattern.

We might say here that under these conditions we'll forget the ball-bank indicator, because we don't care how much we skid in holding our wings level. What we're interested in is *positive control.*

This gives us our second rule: *Hold the wings level by reference to the turn-needle.*

All right. This takes care of directional attitude control—holding the wings level. We also want to hold the nose level, control up-and-down attitude. The instrument we'll use for this chore is the airspeed indicator. But we'll read it differently than we do the turn indicator. Whereas we keep the turn-needle exactly centered (or "average-center" in rough air), it is the airspeed needle's *tendency* which interests us in keeping the nose level.

If the airspeed needle is moving up the scale, indicating higher readings, we are of course in a nose-down attitude. We are diving. The faster it winds up—that is, the speed with which the needle moves—the steeper our dive.

Conversely, if the airspeed needle is moving backward, showing successively slower speeds, then we are in a nose-high attitude; and the speed with which the needle drops back is an indication of how steeply our nose is pointed upward.

In other words, when the airspeed needle remains constant, your nose is level.

In all cases, use the light, relaxed—who's relaxed at a time like this?—anyway, use light control pressures on the wheel and rudder pedals, rather than "manhandling." Overcontrolling means that the overcontrol must be corrected, and this can become a vicious circle.

Now that we know how to keep the airplane straight and level and under control, the next thing is to turn around and go back—straight and level and under control.

First, what is our reciprocal heading? (If we did a good job of flight planning before take-off, we won't be forced to do mental arithmetic under pressure now. We'll not only have the figure ready, but a heading to an alternate as well.) Our reciprocal is 225°? Okay. Apply a little rudder pressure, just enough to move the turn-needle one-half its width. A "one-half needle" turn is equal to one-and-a-half degrees of turn per second. This means that your 180° turn to reciprocal will take exactly two minutes. This gives us our third important rule: *A one-half needle turn continued for two minutes equals a 180° change in direction.*

(We should explain here that some instructors prefer to use the "full needle-width" turn. This results in a 180° change of direction in one minute, because the rate-of-turn is three degrees per second. The disadvantage of this faster turn, as we see it, is that it gets your wing down twice as far.)

At the end of two minutes, center the turn-needle again and, as soon as the magnetic compass settles down, check to see if we've hit our desired 225° reciprocal. If not, use a little rudder to make the necessary slight correction.

An important point to remember in this method of attitude control is to follow the sequence: First, center the turn-needle; second, steady the airspeed needle. These two things are repeated over and over until you are VFR again.

We've not yet mentioned the use of throttle or trim. Attention to them is minimized because the chief value of this method lies in its simplicity.

Forget trim. Changes of trim under these conditions can give the non-instrument pilot more trouble than benefit. Nor should it be necessary to adjust the throttle more than once.

Immediately upon finding yourself on instruments, set the throttle at about 10 per cent below normal cruise. This will slow you down a little and ease wing loadings if turbulence is present. Also, it will slow down the airspeed needle's gains and losses, making these tendencies easier to correct without overcontrolling.

Summing up the important points:

1) Reduce throttle setting to about 10 per cent below normal cruise.

2) Center the turn-needle.

3) Steady the airspeed needle.

4) Endlessly repeat points 2) and 3).

5) A one-half needle turn, continued for two minutes, equals a 180° change in direction.

It is possible, because of unusual turbulence or even panic, temporarily to lose control of the plane while flying blind. If this should happen, the attitude-control method explained here is still the quickest and safest way for the non-instrument pilot to regain command of the airplane. First—everlastingly first—center the turn-needle. But if the plane has gotten away from you and is diving at high speed, it will be desirable to close the throttle before easing the wheel back. As the airspeed drops back to near normal, you will feed in the power again. Then repeat the "old one-two": Center the turn-needle, and steady the airspeed needle.

It may pay big dividends someday if you'll spend some hours practicing these procedures. You can do it in your plane, or a Link Trainer, where all your crashes are imaginary. We should note, too, that this knowledge could prove valuable in other ways. Night flying, even in reasonably good weather, can produce situations where visual ground-reference is tricky.

Finally, there is no substitute for good judgment. Remain

on the ground when the weather is marginal, or recognize trouble ahead and turn back before it's too late. However, the technique described above is good to know because, well, after all, people are people.

Happy landings!

Chronology of Firsts

Chronology of Firsts

Some significant contributions to our mastery of the air are listed below:

Egypt, 150 B.C. *Principle of Jet Propulsion*
Hero, with his aeolipile, demonstrated the fundamentals upon which the modern jet aircraft flies.

Italy, 1496 A.D. *First Mechanical Flying Machine*
Leonardo da Vinci developed the principle of the airplane propeller, the helicopter, and the parachute.

England, 1680 *Jet Propulsion Applied*
Sir Isaac Newton carried out experiments in jet propulsion with a wheeled vehicle.

France, 1783 *First Balloon Flight*
Etienne and Joseph Montgolfier successfully launched an unmanned hot-air balloon.

France, 1855 *First Successful Glider Flight*
Jean Marie La Bris made a glide of one-eighth of a mile in a machine patterned after an albatross.

California, 1884 *First U.S. Glider Flight*
John J. Montgomery accomplished the first flight employing artificial wings in the United States.

Germany, 1899-1900 *First Zeppelin*
Count Ferdinand von Zeppelin designed and built first rigid airship. It was flown at a speed of eight and one-half miles per hour.

WRIGHT BROTHERS' BIPLANE: The world's first successful airplane was powered with a 12 h.p. engine designed and built by the Wrights. Two chain-driven propellers were mounted behind the wings. The pilot lay prone on the lower wing beside the engine, and the horizontal stabilizers stuck out in front on booms.

North Carolina, 1903   First Successful Airplane

Orville Wright was first to fly an airplane, covering 120 feet in twelve seconds. Later the same day, December 17, his brother Wilbur flew 852 feet in fifty-nine seconds.

France, 1909   English Channel Crossing

Louis Blériot accomplished the world's first official international flight, from France to England. His time was thirty-seven minutes for the thirty-one miles.

United States, 1910   First "Carrier" Take-off

Eugene Ely, using a specially-constructed ramp, took off from the USS *Birmingham*.

United States, 1911   First Transcontinental Flights

Robert C. Fowler flew from San Francisco to Jacksonville, and Calbraith Rodgers flew the *Vin Fizz* (named for a soft-drink of that day) from Long Island to Pasadena, in eighty-four hours flying time.

United States, 1914   Establishment of U.S. Air Force

The U.S. Army Air Service, a section created within the Signal Corps, began operation with sixteen officers, seventy-seven men, and eight airplanes.

WORLD WAR I FIGHTER-BOMBER: The De Havilland DH4, designed by the same man responsible for today's De Havilland Comets. Ninety-five per cent of all warplanes built in the U.S. during World War I were DH4's. The pilots who flew this plane in 1917 and 1918 called it "The Flaming Coffin."

Canada, 1919   *First Nonstop Transatlantic Flight*

Captain John Alcock and Lt. A. W. Brown flew a twin-engined Vickers bomber nonstop from St. Johns, Nova Scotia, to Clifden, Ireland; almost two thousand miles in sixteen hours.

United States, 1924   *First World Flight*

Lt. Lowell Smith and Lt. E. H. Nelson, piloting Douglas Army biplanes, completed the first air journey around the world. Each covered a distance of 26,345 miles, returning to their Seattle, Washington, starting point in 175 days.

United States, 1926   *First Multi-engined Metal Airliner*

William B. Stout designed the first multi-engined, all-metal airliner. Produced by the Ford Motor Company, more than twenty of the original two hundred are still flying.

United States, 1927   *New York to Paris Solo Flight*

Charles A. Lindbergh flew in a Wright-powered Ryan monoplane, *The Spirit of St. Louis,* from Roosevelt Field, Long Island, to Le Bourget Field, Paris, a distance of 3,610 miles, in thirty-three hours and thirty-nine minutes. This achievement by a modest and courageous young man captured the fancy of the public and opened the door to aviation's Golden Age.

United States, 1933   *Solo World Flight*

Wiley Post, a one-eyed barnstorming pilot from Oklahoma, flew around the world in seven days and eighteen hours in the Lockheed monoplane, *Winnie Mae.*

Germany, 1937   *First Successful Helicopter*

Dr. Heinrich Focke designed and built the first controllable helicopter, the FW-61.

Italy, 1940   *First Jet Airplane to Fly*

The Caproni-Campini, flown by Capt. Giovanni Pedace, attained a speed of 160 mph near Turin. This airplane em-

BYRD EXPEDITION PLANE: Commander Richard E. Byrd chose the "Tin Goose" (Ford Tri-Motor, Model 4-AT) for his first South Pole expedition. Powered with three 200 h.p. Wright engines, the Ford could get into and out of the proverbial pea patch— and often needed to. Pilots claimed it would "haul all you can cram inside and tie outside." Early models had open cockpits, with the twelve venturesome passengers riding comfortably (?) inside.

ployed an ordinary gasoline engine to drive a two-stage compressor.

United States, 1947   Speed of Sound Exceeded
Capt. Charles Yeager, flying the Bell X-1 rocket plane, exceeded the speed of sound in level flight.

United States, 1957   Transcontinental Jet Record
Marine Major John Glenn Jr. flew an F8U-1 Crusader from Los Alamitos, Calif., Naval Air Station, to Floyd Bennett Field, New York, in 3 hours, 23 minutes, 8.4 seconds.

He refueled in the air three times from tanker planes, and averaged about 55 mph faster than sound for the entire trip.

(Major Glenn, now Colonel, is one of that select group of seven astronauts from which the first American spaceman will be chosen.)

Russia, 1957   First Artificial Earth Satellite

On October 5, Russian scientists sent an unmanned satellite into polar orbit about the earth.

United States, 1959   First Space Airplane

The 3,600 mph X-15, built by North American Aviation Company, began preliminary test flights.

United States, 1959   World Lightplane Record

These days, a non-stop flight of 7,668 miles—from Morocco to Los Angeles—scarcely raises an eyebrow; but when such a feat is accomplished in a four-place business plane, piloted by a grandfather of some fifty-odd years, we're at least reminded how far flying has progressed since the "crazy" Wright Brothers coaxed their flimsy machine into the air less than sixty years ago. Max Conrad's flight in a Piper Comanche established a new world record for lightplanes. He stretched the Comanche's normal range by replacing the three empty seats with 460 gallons of extra gas. At take-off, the single-engine Comanche lifted nearly three and one-half times its own weight.

A Gallery of Planes

AEROCAR: This two-place car-plane is powered with a 143 h.p. Lycoming engine which, coupled with fluid drive, gives this unique machine an air cruise of 105 mph, and a top road-speed of 67 mph. Metal wings and tail are quickly detachable from the Fiberglas cabin, and may be left at the airport or towed as a trailer. The prop is located behind the tail surfaces. Price: $12,500. Aerocar, Inc., Longview, Washington.

138

MORRISEY, MODEL 2150: Another brand-new plane for training, personal, and business use. It is two-place, powered with a 150 h.p. Lycoming; stable and honest to fly, it has lines that should please those with a touch of the fighter-pilot's instincts. It cruises at 135 mph, and climbs 1,450 feet per minute. Price: $8,150. Morrisey Aviation, Inc., Santa Ana, California.

AERONCA: Affectionately known to thousands of pilots as the "Air-knocker," this two-place tandem trainer is no longer in production. However, the Champion Aircraft Company of Osceola, Wisconsin, is manufacturing the Sky Trac, a direct descendant of this old stand-by, which greatly resembles its predecessor. The Sky Trac is powered with a 140 h.p. Lycoming. Its range is 635 miles. Cruise: 115 mph. Top speed: 125 mph. Price: $6,550.

TRECKER 166: A new plane to challenge the hard-to-beat Aero Commander. Designed for company executives, the 166 offers a wide choice of interiors ranging from six to eight seats. Sixty-gallon tip tanks give a range of 1,155 miles. Cruise is 208 mph; top speed, 225 mph. Power is twin Lycomings of 340 h.p. each. Trecker Aircraft Corp., Milwaukee, Wisconsin.

141

TRECKER GULL: A five-place, twin-engine amphibian, the Gull has a range of 994 miles, a cruising speed of 179 mph, and a top speed of 208 mph. Its engines are 340 h.p. Lycomings. This plane is widely used by the Italian Air Force for coastal patrol duty. Trecker Aircraft Corp., Milwaukee, Wisconsin.

142

SILVAIRE LUSCOMBE: All metal, two-place with conventional gear, a fine performer. Engine is 90 h.p. Continental. Top speed is 128 mph, best cruise is 120 mph. Range: 500 miles. Price: $4,950. A popular float plane. Silvaire Aircraft Co., Fort Collins, Colorado.

143

TUSCO NAVION: This well-designed aircraft was originally produced by North American Aviation. Production stopped several years ago, but the Tusco Corporation has slicked them up a little and is offering a like-new conversion, complete with tip tanks, for $15,000. The Navion is all metal, four-place, with a 240 h.p. Continental engine. Its maximum speed is 185 mph, and its best cruise 170 mph. Tusco Corp., Galveston, Texas. (Pictured here is unconverted Navion, without exterior wingtip tanks.)

144

CallAir A-5: The CallAir agricultural plane at work. This plane is not a conversion, but designed for dusting and spraying of crops. It is two-place, the "loader" riding behind the pilot, facing toward the rear and tending the dust hopper or spray tank.

Engine: 150 h.p. Lycoming. Top speed: 104 mph. Cruise: 82 mph. Will cover seven acres per minute with spray or dust. Price: $10,500. CallAir, Inc., Afton, Wyoming.

BEECH TRAVELAIR, MODEL 95: Newest and smallest of Beech's several twin-engine planes, it has reputation for quietness inside. Four-place. Powered with two Lycomings at 180 h.p. Its range is 1,410 miles, best cruise 195 mph, and top speed 210 mph. Price: $51,500. Beech Aircraft Corp., Wichita, Kansas.

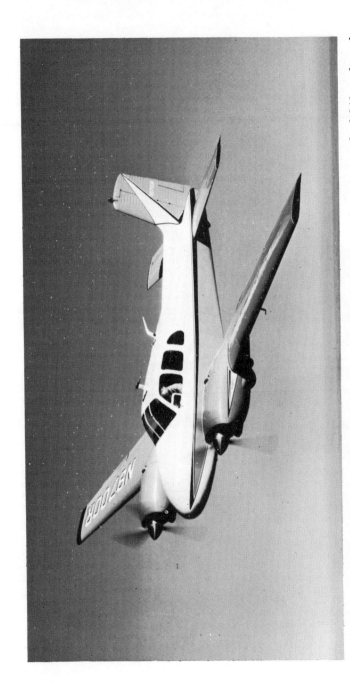

BEECH TWIN-BONANZA G50: A rugged, comfortable executive aircraft, the Twin-Bonanza seats six, has a range of 1,720 miles. Its engines are 340 h.p. Ly- comings which give it a top speed of 240 mph and a cruise of 228 mph. It's priced at $95,000. Beech Aircraft Corp., Wichita, Kansas.

147

BEECHCRAFT BONANZA, MODEL K35: Latest in a long line of record-breaking lightplanes, is powered with a 250 h.p. Continental engine equipped with fuel injection. Four-place, with a range of 1,245 miles, its best cruise is 200 mph, and its top speed is 210 mph. $25,300. Beech Aircraft Corp., Wichita, Kansas.

BEECH SUPER 18: Model E18S is a plush, eight-passenger executive plane equipped with 450 h.p. Pratt & Whitney engines and full feathering pro-pellers. Its range is 1,626 miles at 215 mph. Its top speed is 234 mph. $126,000. Beech Aircraft Corp., Wichita, Kansas.

149

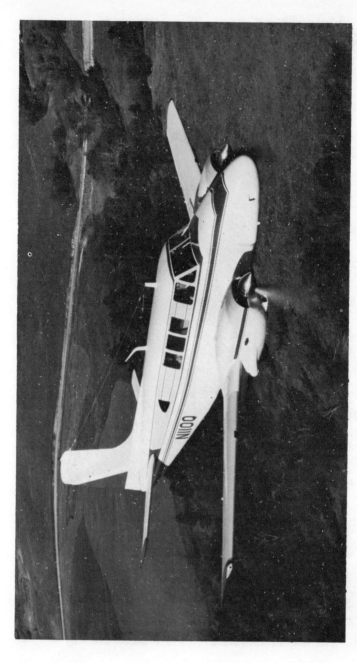

BEECHCRAFT QUEEN AIR 65: This craft is powered by two Lycoming 320 h.p. engines. Cruising speed is 214 mph, maximum is 239 mph. Has a range of 1,445 miles. Beech Aircraft Corp., Wichita, Kansas.

BEECHCRAFT DEBONAIR 33: Powered by 225 h.p. Continental engine, this four-placer has a range of 1,170 miles, cruising speed of 143 mph and top speed of 195 mph. Beech Aircraft Corp., Wichita, Kansas.

MOONEY MARK 20: This trim four-placer gives more speed per horsepower than any other lightplane. Powered with a 180 h.p. Lycoming, it has a top speed of 190 mph and cruises at 180 mph. It has a range of 1,075 miles. Sells for $17,000. Mooney Aircraft, Inc., Kerrville, Texas.

152

FORNAIRE EXPLORER: The two-place Fornaire is considered the easiest to fly of all aircraft. It has no rudder pedals, and the rudders are interconnected with the aileron controls. Thus slips, skids, and spins are impossible. Cheap to fly and maintain, the Fornaire is an excellent personal plane. It has a 90 h.p. Continental in the nose, giving it a top speed of 126 mph, a cruising speed of 121 mph. Its range is 500 miles. $6,995. Forney Aircraft, Fort Collins, Colorado.

153

CESSNA SKYLANE: Cessna's plush four-placer. Powered with 230 h.p. Continental engine, it has a top speed of 170 mph, cruises at 160, and has a range of 845 miles. $17,095. Cessna Aircraft Corp., Wichita, Kansas.

154

CESSNA 150: This proud little two-seater is all metal, a good first plane for newly-licensed pilots. Its power plant is a 100 h.p. Continental which gives it a top speed of 124 mph, and a recommended cruise of 121 mph. Its range is 630 miles, and it is priced at $6,995. Cessna Aircraft Corp., Wichita, Kansas.

CESSNA 172: A roomy, four-place plane, featuring Cessna's famous Para-lift flaps and easy-landing spring steel landing gear. The engine is a 145 h.p. Continental, giving a maximum speed of 135 mph and a cruising speed of 124 mph. It has a range of 620 miles. Price: $9,250. Cessna Aircraft Corp., Wichita, Kansas.

CESSNA 175: A four-place, all-metal plane. It is powered with a 175 h.p. Continental engine, giving it a top speed of 147 mph, and a maximum recommended cruise of 139 mph. Range is 720 miles, priced at $11,250. Cessna Aircraft Corp., Wichita, Kansas.

CESSNA 180: A high performance lightplane with conventional landing gear, making it ideal for short rough fields. The 230 h.p. Continental swings a constant-speed prop and trues out at 170 mph top speed at sea level. It cruises at 160 mph and has a range of 845 miles. $14,250. Cessna Aircraft Corp., Wichita, Kansas.

158

CESSNA 182: Essentially the same plane as the 180, except that it is equipped with tricycle landing gear. Seats four. Nose wheel costs about 3 mph, thus top speed is 167 mph and cruise is 157. Price: $14,600. Cessna Aircraft Corp., Wichita, Kansas.

159

CESSNA 210: Latest addition to Cessna's line of single-engine aircraft (production began September, 1959), the 210 has a retractable tricycle landing gear. It is four-place, powered with the 260 h.p. Continental fuel injection engine, and cruises at 190 mph. Price not available. Cessna Aircraft Corp., Wichita, Kansas.

160

CESSNA 310C: Often called "the most beautiful light twin in the world," the sleek 310C has performance to match her looks. She'll climb 440 feet per minute on one engine, for example. Her engines are Continentals, of 260 h.p. each. Her top speed at sea level is 242 mph; maximum cruise, 220 mph. Seats five and has a range of 1,440 miles. Price: $59,950. Cessna Aircraft Corp., Wichita, Kansas.

CESSNA 310D: New styling of Cessna's 1960 Model 310D is illustrated with the exterior design of the swept vertical fin. The 310D is powered by dual Continental 260 h.p. engines with fuel injection, providing the airplane with a cruising speed of 220 mph and a 440-foot-per-minute rate of climb on only one engine. Cessna Aircraft Corp., Wichita, Kansas.

162

AERO COMMANDER 560-E: Designed for executive use. Seats five to seven. Two Lycoming engines of 295 h.p. each. Maximum speed, 225 mph; best cruise, 210 mph. Range 1,625 miles. Price: $78,500. Aero Design & Engineering Co., Bethany, Oklahoma.

163

BELLANCA 260: Another new plane, the 260 is Fiberglas covered, with a retractable tricycle gear. Seats four. Cruises at 203 mph, with a top speed of 208 mph. The engine is Continental's 260 h.p. fuel injection model. Range is 880 miles. Price: $18,990. Downner Aircraft Industries, Inc., Alexandria, Minnesota.

164

SKY GEM: This is a brand-new, all-metal four-placer with impressive performance. Its engine is a 204 h.p. Continental. It has a maximum range of 985 miles, and recommended cruising speed with full load is 180 miles per hour. Price still unannounced. Gem Aircraft, Inc., Rexburg, Idaho.

165

COLONIAL SKIMMER C-2: A four-place amphibian is 500 miles, and best cruise speed is 130 mph. Price: powered with a Lycoming 180 h.p. engine. Its range $21,895. Colonial Aircraft Corp., Sanford, Maine.

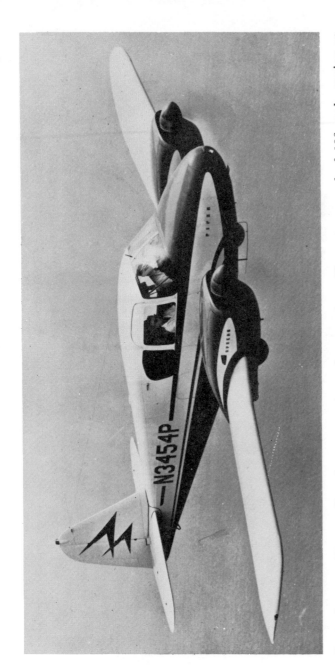

PIPER APACHE: The smallest, least expensive twin in the market. More than fifty Apaches have flown the Atlantic in the process of overseas delivery. Seats five, is powered with a pair of 160 h.p. Ly-comings. Has a top speed of 183 mph, cruises at 171 mph, and has a normal range of 853 miles. Price: $36,990. Piper Aircraft Corp., Lock Haven, Pennsylvania.

167

PIPER COMANCHE: The graceful swept-tail tips off the eagerness of this four-placer. With a 180 h.p. Lycoming (top), it has a top speed of 167 mph, a cruise of 160, and a range of 920 miles. Price: $14,995. The additional 70 h.p. of a 250 Lycoming (bottom) affords a top speed of 190 mph, and a cruise of 181 mph. This faster Comanche has a range of 1,100 miles and sells for $18,995. Piper Aircraft Corp., Lock Haven, Pennsylvania.

168

PIPER PA-18 SUPER CUB: The honest and reliable Cub has been prettied up and sports a plastic Dura-clad finish. It is available in two models. With a 90 h.p. Continental engine, it cruises at 100 mph, has a top speed of 112 and range of 360 miles, and sells for $5,850. With a 150 h.p. Lycoming, it cruises at 115 mph, has a top of 130 and range of 460 miles, and sells for $7,450. Both are two place. Piper Aircraft Corp., Lock Haven, Pennsylvania.

Piper PA-22 Tri-Pacer: A versatile four-place plane, at home anywhere—rugged enough for ranch work, economical enough for family commuting, forgiving enough for the student, and fast enough for the businessman. A 160 h.p. Lycoming gives it a top speed of 141 mph, a cruise of 130, range of 536 miles. Price: $8,890. Piper Aircraft Corp., Lock Haven, Pennsylvania.

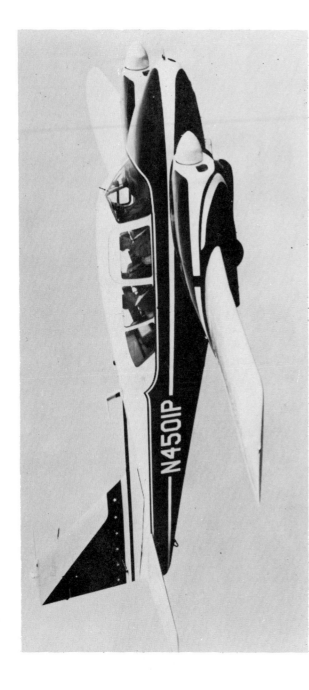

PIPER AZTEC: Newest, largest, fastest airplane in Piper's fleet of business aircraft, the Aztec cruises at over 200 mph and has highest single-engine ceiling of any airplane in its class carrying a similar payload. Powered with two 250 h.p. Lycoming engines, it has a 4,800-pound gross weight, 2,025-pound useful load. Has five-place capacity, full instrumentation, and complete dualized electrical, hydraulic, and vacuum systems. Price, less radio: $49,500.

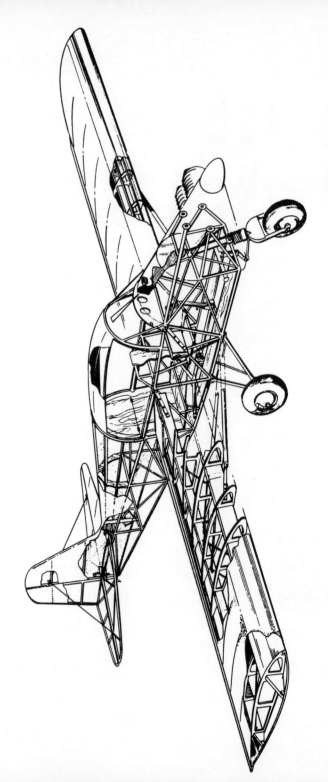

172

STITS FLUT-R-BUG, MODEL SA-6B: For build-it-yourself enthusiasts, Stits Aircraft provides kits and blueprints for several models, which are licensed as amateur-built airplanes. The Flut-R-Bug pictured above has a wing span of 26 feet, length of 18, and ranges over 250 miles. With a 65 h.p. Continental engine, it cruises at 90 mph, has a top speed of 100 mph, and climbs at the rate of over 1,000 feet per minute. With a 90 h.p. Continental its cruise speed is 105 mph; top speed, 115 mph; rate of climb over 1,000 feet per minute. Cost for materials: $750. Stits Aircraft, Riverside, California.

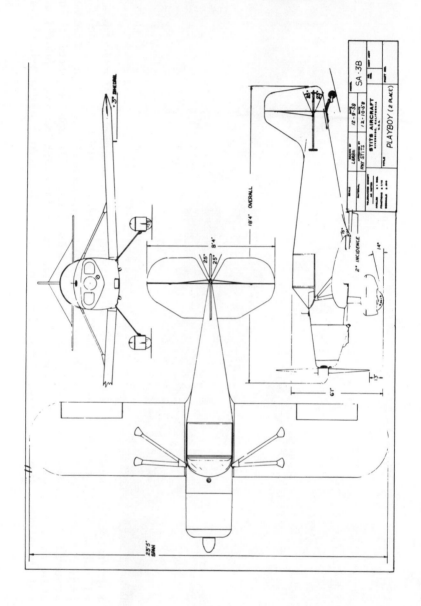

Stits Playboy: This home-built two-placer has a wing span of over 24 feet, length of nearly 18 feet, and is designed for Lycoming engines from 100 to 180 h.p. This one, with 150 h.p. engine, has a cruise speed of 135 mph and top speed of 150 mph; rate of climb is over 1,000 feet per minute. Cost for materials: $1,100. Stits Aircraft, Riverside, California.

Glossary

Glossary

AILERONS: Hinged control surfaces, on outboard trailing edges of the wings, which control angle-of-bank.

AIRFOIL: Any external surface on an aircraft which is designed to react to the air through which it moves, e.g., wings, tail.

AIR MASS: A vast amount of air, usually on the move, which is of a different temperature than the air in its path.

AIR PRESSURE: The weight of air at rest, or the force of its impact if in motion or relative motion.

AIRSPEED: The speed of an aircraft in relation to the air which supports it.

AIRSPEED INDICATOR: An instrument calibrated in knots or miles per hour, which measures the speed relative to the air which supports the machine.

AIRWAY: Numbered corridors of airspace connecting principal air terminals along which lights and radio aids assist navigation.

AIRWORTHINESS CERTIFICATE: A legal paper certifying an aircraft to be structurally sound. Obtained by periodic FAA inspection.

ALTERNATE AIRPORT: An emergency destination preselected by the pilot in the event his original destination is closed by weather.

ALTIMETER: An instrument for measuring air density, and employed in determining altitude.

ALTO-CUMULUS: White, fleecy cloud formation which forms between 8,000 and 20,000 feet above sea level.

ALTO-STRATUS: Hazy and shapeless cloud formation forming between 8,000 and 20,000 feet above sea level.

ANGLE OF ATTACK: The angle at which the leading edge of the wing strikes the supporting sea of air.

ATTITUDE: The position of the airplane's axes in relation to the ground.

AXES: The pivot points about which changes of attitude of an airplane occur.

BANK: Attitude resulting from displacement of wings from horizontal.

BAROMETER: Instrument employed in measuring air pressure.

BASE LEG: The second of three legs, or sides, of an airport landing pattern, connecting the downwind leg with the final approach.

BEAM: A directional radio signal, broadcast as an aid to air navigation.

BEARING: The direction of one point, relative to another, measured in degrees.

CAMBER: The curve of an airfoil viewed in cross-section.

CEILING: Average height, above the surface, of overcast or broken overcast.

CENTER OF GRAVITY: Balance point of airplane where axes converge.

CHECK POINTS: Prominent landmarks preselected by pilot to aid in maintaining track while navigating by pilotage.

CIRRO-CUMULUS: Small, white fleecy clouds made of ice crystals, which form above 20,000 feet.

CIRRO-STRATUS: Thin, milky haze above 20,000 feet.

CIRRUS: Streamers of lacy ice-crystal cloud above 20,000 feet.

COMPASS DEVIATION: Error introduced into magnetic compass by masses of metal or radio equipment in aircraft.

COMPASS HEADING: The figure which is followed on the magnetic compass after corrections have been made for wind, variation, and deviation.

COMPASS ROSE: A circle, marked off along its outer edge with the points of the compass.

COMPUTER: A circular slide rule employed by pilots in calculating navigational problems.

CONE OF SILENCE: A cone-shaped area, vertex at the bottom, above a low-frequency beam radio transmitter, in which no signal is heard.

CONSTANT SPEED PROPELLER: A propeller which automatically adjusts its blade pitch to conform with a preselected rpm setting made by the pilot.

CONTOUR LINES: Lines drawn on an air chart to denote terrain elevation.

CONTROL AREA: The airspace lying within a civil airway.

CONTROLLABLE PROPELLER: A propeller so equipped that its blade pitch may be manually adjusted by pilot in flight.

CONTROL ZONE: The airspace above an airport and its immediate environs.

CUMULO-NIMBUS: A cumulus cloud which has taken on vertical development and become a thunderhead.

CUMULUS: A fleecy, sheeplike cloud which forms at the upper end of a rising current of air.

DEVIATION: See COMPASS DEVIATION.

DEVIATION CARD: A small card, placed near the magnetic compass, which lists deviation corrections for principal headings.

DEW POINT: The temperature at which a given mass of air becomes saturated with moisture.

DOWNWIND LEG: The first of three legs, or sides, of an airport landing pattern, paralleling the runway, and flown in an opposite direction to that in which the landing is to be made.

ELEVATORS: Hinged rear portion of horizontal tail surfaces.

E.T.A.: Estimated time of arrival.

FIN: The fixed forward portion of the vertical tail surface.

FINAL APPROACH: The third of three legs of an airport landing pattern; the final leg, in which the aircraft is lined up with the runway for touching down.

FLAPS: Hinged surfaces below inboard trailing edge of wings.

FRONT: The dividing line between an advancing mass of air, and the air of different temperature in its path.

FRONTOGENESIS: A front that is forming.

FRONTOLYSIS: A front that is dissipating.

FUEL SELECTOR SWITCH: A switch which allows pilot to select manually fuel tank from which fuel is to be used.

GREAT CIRCLE COURSE: The shortest distance between two points on the surface of a globe.

GREENWICH MERIDIAN: An imaginary great circle line between the earth's poles, which passes through Greenwich, England. Also called the Zero Meridian.

GROUND SPEED: The speed the plane is making in relation to the ground.

HIGH PRESSURE AREA: An air mass composed of denser air than that which surrounds it.

HORIZONTAL AXIS: An imaginary line, running from wingtip to wingtip, about which the nose swings upward and downward.

HORIZONTAL STABILIZER: The fixed, forward portion of the horizontal tail surfaces.

HUMIDITY: The amount of moisture, measured in per cent, that a given mass of air contains in proportion to that which it could contain if saturated.

ICE, CARBURETOR: Ice which forms in the carburetor throat due to rapid expansion of air entering the intake manifold of engine.

INDICATED AIRSPEED: The figure registered on the airspeed indicator.

IFR: Instrument flight rules.

ISOBARS: Lines of equal pressure drawn on the weather map.

ISOGONIC LINES: The uneven lines of magnetic force as charted from magnetic north.

KNOT: 1.15 miles per hour.

LAPSE RATE, NORMAL: The steady decrease of temperature with altitude. The rate is $3\frac{1}{2}$ degrees per 1,000 feet.

LATITUDE: A position on the surface of a globe in relation to north and south.

LEADING EDGE: The foremost or front edge of a wing or tail surface.

LIGHT SIGNALS: Signals employed, in lieu of radio, by air traffic controllers in the tower.

LINE SQUALL: A line of heavy thunderstorms, often traveling several miles ahead of a cold front.

LOGBOOK: An official record of a pilot's flight time.

LONGITUDE: A position on the earth's surface, in relation to east and west. The Greenwich Meridian is used as a starting point.

LONGITUDINAL AXIS: An imaginary center line, running from nose to tail of an airplane, about which the plane is rolled to produce a bank.

LOW PRESSURE AREA: An air mass of less density than the air which surrounds it.

MAGNETIC NORTH: The geographical point, in northern Canada, which attracts the magnetic compass.

MAGNETO: A mechanically driven generator which furnishes the electrical impulses required for engine ignition.

MERIDIANS: Imaginary great-circle lines which run vertically around the earth and converge at the poles. They are used to determine longitude.

MID-MERIDIAN: That meridian, on an air chart, nearest to halfway between a given departure point and destination.

MILLIBAR: Unit of measure in determining air pressure. 1013.2 millibars = 29.92 inches of mercury, which is standard atmospheric pressure at sea level at 59° F.

MOMENT, PITCHING: Movement of plane's attitude about its horizontal axis; e.g., nose up–nose down.

MOMENT, ROLLING: Movement of plane's attitude about its longitudinal axis; e.g., banking.

MOMENT, YAW: Movement of plane's attitude about its vertical axis; e.g., the swinging of the nose to one side or another.

NIMBO-STRATUS: Dark, shapeless and ragged layer of cloud, usually very low, from which rain or snow is likely to fall.

PARALLEL OF LATITUDE: Imaginary horizontal lines around

the earth employed to establish latitude.

PILOTAGE: Navigation of aircraft by reference to compass, check points, and elapsed time. Also called contact navigation.

PITOT HEAD: A small tube, usually located below left wing, with open end facing forward to receive relative wind. The resulting pressure is recorded on the airspeed indicator in mph.

PLOTTER: Combination ruler-protractor of transparent plastic employed in plotting course and heading.

PREFLIGHT CHECK: Exterior inspection of aircraft before flight.

RELATIVE WIND: The flow of air past an aircraft created by the machine's forward movement.

RPM: Revolutions per minute. The rate at which the engine's crankshaft revolves.

RUDDER: The rearmost, hinged portion of the vertical tail surface.

RUDDER PEDALS: Foot-pedals in the cockpit which control the rudder.

SELECTOR SWITCH: See FUEL SELECTOR SWITCH.

SPIN (TAILSPIN): An uncontrolled, corkscrewing dive common in earlier planes as a result of a stall. Modern light-planes will not spin accidentally; some cannot be forced.

SPIRAL: A descending series of circles.

SQUALL LINE: See LINE SQUALL.

STATION MODEL: Weather map symbol representing weather reporting station and listing its observations.

STRATO-CUMULUS: Low grayish clouds forming in rolls or waves.

STRATUS: Uniform layer of low fog not touching the ground.

TACHOMETER: Gauge which registers the engine rpm.

THERMAL: A heated, rising column of air.

TORQUE: Combined effects of the twisting column of air produced by the propeller, and the propeller's reaction on the engine mountings.

TRACK: An imaginary line over the surface coinciding with the airplane's path of flight.

TRIM: Adjustment of auxiliary flight control surfaces, such as the horizontal stabilizer, which allows a plane to be trimmed, i.e., dynamically balanced.

TRUE AIRSPEED: Airspeed indicator reading corrected for altitude and air temperature errors.

TRUE COURSE: Direction, measured in degrees, in which a given destination lies.

VARIATION: The difference, measured in degrees, between true north and magnetic north.

VENTURI: A venturi tube narrows part-way from one end and then flares to greater diameter again. In a carburetor throat, this has the effect of compressing the fuel-air mist for better mixing and increased efficiency.

VERTICAL AXIS: An imaginary line, running perpendicularly through the airplane's center of gravity, about which the plane's nose swings to left or right.

VISIBILITY: Average distance, from the cockpit, that prominent objects may be seen.

VFR: Visual flight rules.

VOR: Abbreviation for Very High Frequency Omni Range Radio System. Also called OMNI.

WARM FRONT: A moving mass of air which is warmer than the air in its path.

WIND CORRECTION ANGLE: Amount of correction, measured in degrees, necessary to compensate for wind effect in maintaining a desired track.

WIND VECTOR: A scale diagram drawn to determine wind correction angle and ground speed.

WING LOADING, DYNAMIC: Wing stress due to rapid change of direction.

WING LOADING, STATIC: Total weight of airplane divided into total wing area.

YAW: The swinging of the aircraft's nose to left or right about its vertical axis.

Index

Numbers set in Italics refer to Illustrations.

188